Home and Away

Adventures in Beekeeping
in the UK and Africa

John Home

Our very Best
Wishes Roy
Mary & John
2013

LIVE WIRE

First published in 2012 by
Live Wire Books
The Orchard, School Lane,
Warmington, Banbury
Oxfordshire OX17 1DE

ISBN 978-0-9553124-6-5

Telephone: 01295 690624
Email: info@livewirebooks.com

Designed by Dick Malt

Photo credits: page 8, courtesy of Brian Durk;
page 59 (Harry Wickens), courtesy of Clive
De Bruyn; page 83, courtesy of David Murray
(www.davidmurray.org); page 84, courtesy of
Richard Stanton; page 105 (Duke of Kent),
courtesy of Simon King; page 128, courtesy of
Claire Waring. Thanks also to Pam Gregory for
allowing the use of several of her photos in the
early chapters.

Printed and bound by CPI Group (UK) Ltd,
Croydon, CR0 4YY.

Contents

Foreword

When John asked me to write this Foreword my reaction was two-fold. Firstly, I was really looking forward to reading his book and, secondly, I felt very privileged that he had approached me to write this brief introduction.

I have known John for more years than I, and probably he, care to remember. We first worked together on the Bees and Honey section at the Royal Show. It was there that I realised what a wealth of knowledge and experience he has, not just to do with bees but also with the beekeeping and farming communities and with life in general.

Real characters seem to be getting thinner and thinner on the ground and yet there are still some gems to be found, and John is one of them. He is a very practical man, whose all-round skills in this respect extend beyond beekeeping to dealing with other problems that arise. He has the ability to 'think outside the box' and come up with workable, if sometimes unorthodox, solutions. As you will read in the pages that follow, this has stood him in good stead in his work for Bees Abroad, for whom he not only took over our original Kenyan project but, along with his wife Mary, went on to extend the work both there and in other areas. He then agreed to take on further commitments as Chairman of the Bees Abroad Management Committee and was also instrumental in helping to establish the Projects Sub-Committee, all this in addition to the heavy demands of his involvement with the Bee Farmers Association.

In his case, it is certainly true that if you want a job done, ask a busy man! If John takes on a task, he is committed to completing it and this is manifestly the case with his Bees Abroad projects. All of us who are working for the charity are spurred on when we see what a difference can be made to people's lives with just a little help to make their beekeeping more profitable. A notable example is the work that John and Mary have done in teaching beekeeping groups to make value-added beeswax products that can be sold for a profit.

Another illustration of John's ability to think outside the box is the way in which he has involved others in the communities where Bees Abroad has set up projects, whether it be in making a-maizing beesuits or in using carpentry skills to produce hives, top bars and other pieces of beekeeping equipment.

In this book, you will get an insight into a very special man, his love of bees and beekeeping and his willingness to share this with others less fortunate than himself. Just one illustration of this is the fact that all the profits from this book will not go to the author but to help fund the work that he and Mary are doing in Kenya. I heartily commend it and the work of Bees Abroad to you.

Claire Waring
Editor of *Bee Craft* and Founding Trustee of Bees Abroad

Bus travel in Africa - not for the faint-hearted

1: New Horizons

The road to hell? Never mind the M25 in the rush hour, or the M6 when the juggernaut articulated lorries are out in force. Taking a trip along the main arterial highway from Mombasa in Kenya to the Ugandan capital of Kampala can be a far more testing ordeal, something definitely not recommended for the faint-hearted. The Kenyan section is bad enough, with a wave-like ripple in the surface caused by subsidence and poor foundations making for an extremely uncomfortable ride. But at least the carriageway is just about wide enough to accommodate two-way traffic. It is when you cross the Ugandan border and head into the heart of Africa that the real nightmare begins. Here the busy highway is mostly reduced to a narrow strip of crumbling tarmac that falls away on either side to create an alarmingly steep reverse camber. And with a procession of heavy trucks thundering along at speed in each direction, one's journey develops into an almost continual chicken run as drivers wait to see who will blink first and take to the rough, stony verges in a cloud of dust.

For nervous first-time European passengers, clinging to their seats in one of the ageing minibuses that are the main form of public transport throughout much of rural Africa, it can be a terrifying experience – especially when, as is all too often the case, the man behind the wheel seems intent on proving his credentials as a dare-devil rally driver. Every moment seems destined to be one's last as yet another near miss is followed by the vehicle threatening to tip over as it lurches, bumps and rattles along the verge at a crazy angle, the offside wheels lifting clear of the ground at times while all those inside automatically throw their weight to the opposite side in an effort to bring them back down to earth. That this doesn't always do the trick is a fact borne out by the alarming number of overturned trucks that can be seen lying beside the road. After four or five hours of this sort of roller-coaster action one is likely to be left a physical and emotional wreck.

So what on earth has all this got to do with beekeeping? I would probably have asked the same question myself before I became involved with Bees Abroad. A small specialist charity organisation, this was formed thirteen years ago to promote beekeeping in developing countries around the world, mostly in the poorest parts of Africa, as a sustainable and environmentally sound way of alleviating poverty by providing income, employment and nutrition for families and local communities. And as I was to discover, hair-raising travel experiences go with the territory.

I had just retired as a commercial beekeeper in the UK when Brian Durk, one of the founders of Bees Abroad, recruited me in 2005. I was visiting the National Honey Show and Brian, who was teaching beekeeping skills at Hartpury College in Gloucestershire at the time, approached me to ask what bottling machines I used. When I explained that I was no longer in business, having sold Fosse Way Honey and retired, his eyes lit up. "Ah!" he said. "In that case, you're just the man we are looking for."

Brian is a very persuasive character and almost before I knew it I had been talked into joining Bees Abroad's team of energetic and enthusiastic volunteers. And within a matter of weeks I found myself on a plane bound for Malawi, where I was to observe one of their projects in action. It was the start of a new, exciting and completely unexpected chapter in my life at a time when, at the age of sixty-five, I had been getting ready to settle for something a little less adventurous.

Bees Abroad can actually trace its earliest beginnings back to 1997, when Brian Durk responded to an advert in the magazine *Bees For Development* that had been placed by someone in Cameroon who was seeking expert help in setting up a beekeeping venture there. To raise funding for his initial trip out to Cameroon Brian undertook a sponsored one-mile swim. With some help from fellow beekeeper Pam Gregory, a farmer's wife from West Wales who had been working for the UK National Bee Unit for more than twenty years and who has both a National Diploma in Beekeeping and an MSc in Overseas Rural Development, Brian then spent the next three years laying the foundations of what has gone on to become a very successful business, producing commercial tonnages of honey, providing employment for twenty-seven people and winning a local Best Practice training award.

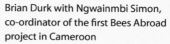

Brian Durk with Ngwainmbi Simon, co-ordinator of the first Bees Abroad project in Cameroon

Me with Pam Gregory

At around the same time that Brian and Pam were getting the Cameroon project up and running, Claire Waring, editor of *Bee Craft* magazine, the official journal of the British Beekeeper's Association, was trying quite independently to do something very similar with some beekeepers she had met while out in Nepal. Pam suggested the two groups get together which they did, combining to form Bees Abroad.

Bees Abroad was officially launched in 1999 and became a registered charity a year later under the chairmanship of the very aptly named Jeff Bee, who had previously been chairman of the Cameroon group. An experienced beekeeper and a good friend of Brian, Pam and Claire, Jeff played a major part in setting up the organisation and getting it off the ground, working enthusiastically to promote it at agricultural shows all around the country and organising a number of successful fund-raising initiatives.

Since its launch, the charity has steadily expanded its activities, setting up further projects in Malawi, Kenya, Uganda, Nigeria, Ghana and Tanzania, with plans to move into Zambia and Zimbabwe. As well as providing training in all aspects of beekeeping – everything from designing and making simple hives to bottling and marketing the honey along with various by-products such as beeswax candles, creams and even medicines – Bees Abroad has often tended to become involved on a much broader level in helping the communities in which it operates. In Nepal, for instance, it has been able

11

to play a part in helping to rescue women from cross-border sex trafficking between Nepal and India, a major problem in the area. Elsewhere, a special project was set up in a local prison with the aim of teaching prisoners beekeeping skills that could possibly provide them with the means to earn a living on their release.

So, although operating on a shoestring budget and on a relatively small localised scale, Bees Abroad can definitely claim to have achieved some very worthwhile results in terms of bringing practical benefits to some of the world's poorest communities, where beekeeping can offer an attractively viable addition to the options available to families and smallholders trying to scratch a living in a subsistence economy. It provides a source of nutrition and income that is relatively easy to introduce, doesn't demand a big start-up investment, doesn't require a large area of land on which to keep hives and is not labour intensive. What's more, in Africa bees mostly come free, so you don't even have to pay to stock your hives. For all these reasons, beekeeping represents an ideal solution to Third World problems.

My previous experience of foreign travel had been limited to a regular annual package holiday with my wife Mary to Tenerife, so it was with a mixture of excitement and slight apprehension that, having been turned into something of a human dartboard by a series of injections as protection against all manner of alarming-sounding diseases, I set out in 2005 on that initial, self-funded trip to Malawi. Pam Gregory had gone out there for a month on one of her regular working visits to the Small Beekeepers Development and Research Association (SBDARA) project that she had started up for Bees Aboard in 2000. She was going to be joined by her husband John for ten days and it was suggested that I should fly out with him to see at first hand what Bees Abroad was really all about.

John and I met up for the first time at Heathrow Airport. I had no idea what he looked like but was told to keep an eye out for somebody walking with a limp caused by a dodgy hip, soon to be replaced. To help him recognise me I sent him a copy of our old Fosse Way Honey leaflet that included a caricature of me sketched by a street artist in Tenerife. Because it made me look a bit whacky this always used to make people laugh – but I guess it must be a pretty good likeness because John straightaway picked me out of the crowded check-in area.

We flew first to Nairobi and then on to Lilongwe, the capital of Malawi. That bit of the journey was fairly straightforward. It was when we then took to a bus to be driven some 200 miles up through Malawi to the SBDARA base at Mkondeze in the Nkhata Bay area that I got my first real taste of Africa.

We hadn't gone very far at all before the bus broke down. As I was soon to discover, this is a fairly regular hazard of driving in the poorer African countries where the roads are rugged, the distances huge and many of the vehicles, especially the buses and taxis, decidedly ancient, with no such thing as an MOT certificate of roadworthiness required. On this occasion we were fortunate that it took only an hour-and-a-half to find a garage and get the clutch repaired.

Back on the road, we drove on until nightfall and shortly thereafter arrived in a village where the driver suddenly pulled up, announced that he was going off to have something to eat and disappeared, leaving us and the rest of his passengers to look after ourselves. The bus was immediately surrounded by vendors trying to sell us everything from iced water to hard boiled eggs. John bought some dried fish and persuaded me, against my better judgement, to give it a try. Dominated by Lake Malawi, which covers nearly 12,000 square miles, Malawi has almost as much water as dry land, so fish is the main source of protein.

The specimen I was handed was about the size of a goldfish and had a rather strange smoky taste. It was only later that I discovered that the locals' preferred method of drying their fish is to drive along with them hanging in front of the radiator grilles of cars, buses and lorries. So they end up being not just dried but diesel smoked! Nibbling away rather tentatively in the darkness I bit on something hard and thought I must have broken a tooth until closer examination in the glow of the bus's sidelights revealed that the offending particle was actually one of the fish's eyeballs! I began to feel slightly queasy.

We eventually arrived at Mkondeze late that night and over the next few days I was given an impressive demonstration of what Pam had managed to achieve with limited resources.

The SBDARA project was one of the first to be set up by Bees Abroad following its launch as an official charity and it remains one of the most

13

successful. Malawi, formerly Nyasaland, is among the world's least developed and poorest countries, with 90% of the largely rural population scratching a living from subsistence farming, more than half of them living below the official poverty line and with the government having to rely heavily on foreign aid.

It was a suggestion from a young Voluntary Service Overseas volunteer called Helen Fox, whose mother happened to be one of Pam's beekeeping students, that led to Bees Abroad getting involved there. While working in Malawi Helen had come into contact with a number of local beekeepers and recognised the development possibilities of what they were doing if only they could get themselves properly organised. She mentioned this to her mother who passed it on to Pam.

As a result, Pam went out on a reconnaissance trip during which she met with around seventy separate groups of beekeepers. She was able to confirm that the miombo woodlands of the northern highlands around Nkhata Bay are ideal for beekeeping, producing a high-calorie, light-coloured honey. At the same time, it was obvious that the local beekeepers were failing to make the most of this potentially valuable resource.

Under Pam's leadership, SBDARA set about putting production onto a sound and sustainable commercial footing, organising beekeepers into democratically-run local groups, providing training, equipment and technical assistance and, perhaps most importantly, setting up the Nkhata Bay Honey Producers Co-operative (NHPC) to market and sell the honey.

Previously, the distance from urban markets and the lack of transport

A traditional bush apiary in Malawi

The early marketing group at SDBARA

Lenson Simumba and George Kamanga with smokers subsidised by Bees Abroad

made it almost impossible for the beekeepers in the villages to get their honey to market and sell it for a good price. They were also being ripped off by rogue traders who would take the honey and then disappear, never to return. Thanks to NHPC that has all changed.

At the last count, there were over a hundred groups operating in villages in the area, with a total of around a thousand individual beekeepers producing up to ten tonnes of honey for sale between them. NHPC buys the honey from them for cash and then bottles, labels, packs, markets and distributes it using the local minibus transport, rented vehicles and, recently, its own one-tonne truck. And it is continually extending its customer base, often supplying its outlying beekeeping groups with recycled mobile phones as a means of helping them to keep in touch.

NHPC trainers

SBDARA, meanwhile, now employs a full-time staff of thirteen, including two local managers – Lenson Simumba and George Kamanga – seven trainers, all of whom have passed the British Beekeepers Association (BBKA) assessment in Basic African Beekeeping, a secretary, a gardener and two night watchmen. In addition it also provides casual employment for builders and labourers, honey packers, two tailors to make protective clothing and a carpenter to help with hive-making.

As well as the obvious benefits it has brought to the beekeepers themselves in terms of a sustainable increase in their income, the project has also, indirectly, had a wider positive effect through encouraging villagers to improve their farming skills generally, boosting food production in the area by encouraging the care of pollinating insects and thereby improving the seed set and quality of crops.

Not surprisingly, it has been welcomed by senior government figures in Malawi, up to and including the President himself, who met the staff in person and who was full of praise for the quality of the honey. Both the Minister of Agriculture and the Minister of Trade have been to Nkhata Bay to see for themselves what has been achieved there. And a TV programme about the work of SBDARA and NHPC has been shown over and over again on Malawi television.

I myself was completely enthralled by what I saw there and came back full of enthusiasm for what Bees Abroad was trying to achieve. It wasn't just that I had seen what a positive difference it could make to people's lives; I was also deeply affected by the attitude of the people themselves and, in particular, the fact that they seemed so content and so happy with so little when we in our affluent society can often be quite miserable with more than enough. I found that quite a humbling experience and it made me even more determined to do my bit to help.

So I didn't hesitate for a moment before saying yes to Pam when she rang me a week or two later to ask if I would consider taking on a project in Kenya that she had started but hadn't got time to carry on with herself.

2: Mad-Tatus and Rude Awakenings

The village of Nessuit is located in the Nakuru district of Kenya's Rift Valley, amid the forested foothills of the Mau Escarpment. It lies on the fringe of what was once known as the White Highlands back in the colonial era when this region was largely taken over by immigrant British farmers, who were attracted by the cooler climate as well as the rich, fertile soils. While the Rift Valley remains one of the more economically advanced provinces in the country, it is now densely populated, putting huge pressure on the natural resources.

A major government resettlement programme involving the relocation of thousands of families to the area around Nessuit has simply added to the problems there. The farming activities of some 20,000 new settlers have caused considerable environmental damage, including the disruption of the Lake Nakuru watershed. With severe drought conditions further aggravating this situation, the lake is drying up and the breeding flamingos that make it an internationally significant wetland site, protected under the Ramsar Convention on wetland conservation, are dying at an alarming rate. At the same time, the insensitive and corrupt way in which land was taken from the indigenous Ogiek people under the resettlement scheme and handed over in five-hectare parcels to farmers from a range of other tribes has led to tension and conflict.

It was against this background that Pam Gregory launched the Bees Abroad project here in 2005 as part of the wider Nessuit Livestock, Beekeeping and Environmental Management scheme (NELBEM). Set up by Weldon Korir, a local Kenyan Customs and Excise officer who had grown up in Nessuit, NELBEM aimed to provide help and support for the poor peasant farmers who had flooded into the area and also to promote sustainable agriculture and rural development.

17

As well as being hunter/gatherers the Ogieks were also beekeepers, so there was already a tradition of beekeeping in the area, mostly involving the use of hollowed-out log hives suspended from trees in the forest. And at Baraka Agricultural College, nearby in Molo, the Bee Development Unit has been offering excellent short courses in beekeeping for some years. Bees Abroad's first move after agreeing to get involved with NELBEM was to pay for twenty people, one from each of twenty local Nessuit beekeeping groups, to go on the one-week course at Baraka, the idea being that they would then come back and pass on the training they had received to the other group members. At the same time, Weldon and project manager Richard Rono, a full-time Health Authority official who, like Weldon, helps to run NELBEM as an unpaid volunteer, had used part of their allowance from Bees Abroad to build, furnish and equip a simple wooden office at the organisation's headquarters in Nessuit. They also created a small, enclosed, one-acre demonstration area where hive-building and other beekeeping skills could be taught and where they went on to plant well over one hundred nectar-bearing fruit and nut trees as well as vegetables that were shared with the community.

This was all up and running by the time I arrived in October 2006 to take over the project and to assess other possible Bees Abroad projects in Kenya that had been put forward for consideration. Pam, along with her husband,

The original committee at NELBEM with Richard Rono (extreme left) and Weldon Korir (in the red shirt).

John, was there to introduce me to the people at Nessuit and I was also accompanied by my wife Mary. Mary paid her own way, but as an ex-nurse and former ward sister who had been heavily involved in helping me to run Fosse Way Honey following her retirement from nursing, she is well-versed on the medicinal and health aspects of honey and its by-products, subjects on which she was able to give valuable talks to the women who, although the men take the lead, are the ones who tend to run the beekeeping groups in Africa.

Mary's first experience of Africa was to prove just as exciting and occasionally even more challenging than mine had been in Malawi the year before. Our trip began relatively comfortably with a warm welcome at Nairobi airport followed by a day-long journey by road up to Njoro, the nearest large town to Nessuit, where, together with Pam and John, we were to be accommodated for the first week in rooms attached to the conference centre at Egerton University. Thankfully, we were able to travel up from Nairobi in our own private minibus rather than having to squash into one of the crowded public transport minibuses known in Kenya as matatus – or 'mad-tatus' as we came to call these often garishly painted and sometimes rather alarmingly overloaded ten-to-twenty-seaters. And our driver, Barnabus, was steadier than most, which was just as well given that the route up through some of the most spectacular parts of the Rift Valley included sections where the road was bordered by massive, hair-raising drops.

When we eventually got to Egerton our accommodation turned out to be relatively luxurious compared with what we were to encounter later in the trip. The beds were clean and came complete with pillows – a rarity in the sort of rooms sometimes provided for Bees Abroad personnel in the field. There were even some showers, although they didn't really work properly. It was when we moved on to a more rural location that conditions generally started to get a bit more challenging. As a farmer's daughter, Mary reckons she can rough it with the best of them, but there were to be times when her nerve and fortitude were quite severely tested! More of that later.

The morning after our arrival we were driven up to Nessuit, our minibus lurching along the dirt track leading up to the project. It was the all-too-familiar white-knuckle ride as what had inevitably been dubbed 'Barney's

'Barney's Bus' on the
road to Nessuit

With the NELBEM group outside their new
headquarters office, and the commemorative
plaque, complete with mis-spellings.

THIS OFFICE WAS OFFICIALLY
OPENED BY PAMELLA GREGORY
AND JOHN HOMES ON 20.10.2006

Bus' negotiated a series of horrific dips and bends made even more difficult
by the deep ruts gouged out by torrential rains.

We finally got there to be welcomed by an enthusiastic and broadly
beaming reception committee led by Weldon Korir and Richard Rono, who
had proudly prepared the office building for an official opening ceremony.
To excited applause, Pam and I together unveiled a simple wooden plaque
to commemorate the occasion, our names rather charmingly mis-spelt for
posterity!

We were delighted with the progress that had been made in the twelve
months since Pam had launched the project. The funding of the course at
Baraka had been a great success. A one-week course can't make you into a
beekeeper – it can only provide an introduction. But in this instance it had
achieved the desired effect of creating a core of people who could pass on
the basic skills they had learned as well as spreading the word about the
possible benefits of beekeeping in the region and getting others interested.
Apart from that, a useful relationship had been established with the people

At Baraka Agricultural College. (Left to right) Tom Carroll, Richard Rono, me and Mary, Pam and John Gregory and Weldon Korir

at Baraka who had offered to provide a number of free training courses for project members.

We spent a day at the college and I was very impressed by the whole set-up there. Baraka was founded and is still run by Franciscans, mostly from Ireland. The college Principal is Brother Tony Dolan and the Bee Development Unit was set up in 1994 by another Irishman, Tom Carroll. The author of a definitive book entitled *A Beginner's Guide to Beekeeping in Kenya*, Tom has worked on beekeeping development not just in Kenya but all over Africa since leaving University College Dublin with a master's degree in agriculture in 1993 and he is passionate about the potential for beekeeping throughout the continent, insisting that bees are actually one of its most undeveloped natural resources.

We were taken on an extensive tour of the whole college as well as being shown around the Bee Development Unit, which includes facilities for hive making and honey bottling and which also has a wax room where candles and cosmetics are made. In addition, the Unit has its own demonstration apiary and bee house, where the various types of hive generally in use in Kenya are on display, all of them occupied by bees.

By far the most popular and practical of these is the Kenyan Top Bar Hive (KTBH), originally developed by the legendary Kenyan beekeeper Peter Paterson, whom we were fortunate enough to meet up with later on during our trip. Simple and inexpensive to make, the KTBH is very attractive to bees and encourages the production of beautiful comb honey. At the same

21

Inspecting a Kenyan Top Bar Hive

Our local artisan carpenter, never without his machete and pencil

time, it has the advantage of being much easier to manage than either a regular European hive – which requires a spinner extractor to harvest the honey, a piece of equipment that is largely unaffordable and unavailable locally – or a traditional African log hive in which the irregular combs stick to the walls and are difficult to harvest without destroying the brood and the entire colony.

There are other reasons why the European hive is not generally suitable for use in Africa. Unlike the KTBH, it cannot easily be suspended high enough off the ground to be safe from the predations of honey badgers or invasion by termites. And it is also vulnerable to colonisation by wax moths whenever the bees move out. We occasionally have problems with the wax moth here in the UK in hot summers but in Africa it is a constant threat. If it happens here and you are left with an empty hive in which all the wax has been eaten by the moths you can get sheets of embossed beeswax foundation to put in the frames and start the bees off again with a new comb. But in the poor rural areas of Africa you can't get hold of that sort of thing for love or money.

Harvesting honey from top bar hives involves simply lifting out the bars and cutting the entire combs off into buckets that are immediately sealed while the bar is replaced. The combs are then taken away and the honey squeezed out and filtered through muslin bags. This system has the added advantage that once you have squeezed out the honey you end up with large quantities of wax for use in a variety of by-products such as candles and hand creams.

Back at Nessuit we had been encouraged to find that around seventy KTBHs had been made and were in use. However, we were told that despite the relatively low cost, there were still problems for some of the poorer group members who couldn't afford even the small amount of wood needed to build them to the specified design. We had a discussion about this during which I suggested that it might be possible to make the hives even more cheaply if the solid wooden sides were dispensed with and replaced by a mixture of sticks and daub, using a similar technique to that used in building the huts they live in.

To help with hive-making, the project had secured the part-time services of a local artisan carpenter, a splendid character who, much to our amusement, kept his pencil tucked into his tight, curly beard rather than behind his ear. He also had a razor-sharp machete almost permanently to hand, suggesting that it might be unwise to argue with him! Although he spoke only Swahili, he realised immediately what I had in mind as soon as I started trying to explain the design modification and the women were duly despatched with washing up bowls to collect mud and cow dung for the daub as well as sticks, maize stalks, bamboo canes and any other material suitable for the framework. To my great satisfaction, it worked perfectly, reducing the cost of making a hive to the point where it was within the reach of even the poorest rural members.

Quite a lot of my time while at Nessuit was spent going on long hikes into the surrounding countryside to visit project members in outlying villages and smallholdings to check their hives and to see how they were getting on with their beekeeping. I don't know whether it has anything to do with Kenyans being great natural long distance runners, but they always seem to underestimate distances. If they tell you as you set out on a walk that the place you are going to is two kilometres away you can bet it will actually turn out to be more like five. In the heat, I sometimes found myself flagging on some of the lengthier walks and took the precaution of marking the route as I went along so that I could find my own way back if I got left behind!

I would mostly be taken to places where there had been problems attracting bees to the hive. The reason was usually something fairly obvious – such as failure to prime the hive properly with beeswax. Or it might be that the hive had not been kept clean and was full of cobwebs. It is also vital to ensure that the top bar is the right width – for ease of measurement, exactly the same as the diameter of a coca cola or beer bottle top. If it is too wide you can end up with 1 ½ combs on a single bar, which is then difficult to lift out.

While I was out in the field, Mary and Pam would spend time with the women members of the project, Mary mostly talking to them about health issues while Pam demonstrated how to use beeswax to make candles and cosmetics such as a basic barrier skin cream. It is generally the women who mostly get involved in beekeeping as the men are often away working.

The unexpected arrival of a freelance national television crew while we were in Nessuit then provided an interesting and ultimately very useful diversion. They chanced upon us while they were filming a news item about the on-going unrest over the re-settlement scheme and were obviously curious about what a bunch of Europeans were doing in such a remote area. Pam and I agreed to be interviewed and took the opportunity to explain how the project was designed to help reduce tribal conflict and unemployment by encouraging people to work together to exploit a valuable natural resource so as to provide a sustainable source of extra income. And we were able to put it over in a very positive way, making the point that we'd seen no evidence of friction despite having people from different tribes within the group. The interview was broadcast the following night, helping to create considerable new interest in the project, prompting a favourable article in the national press and generally raising the profile of the project and the status of Weldon Korir and Richard Rono.

After a week at Nessuit the four of us climbed aboard 'Barney's Bus' once more and were driven more than 100 miles west to Ogembo, near Kisii in the province of Gucca, to visit the Maranatha Family Centre, where we had agreed to help with the setting up of a beekeeping project sponsored by Sherlene Turner, the wife of an Australian beekeeper.

The area around Kisii is very deprived, densely populated and rife with

With Pam Gregory, being interviewed for Kenyan television

HIV/AIDS and the Maranatha Centre is there primarily to look after children orphaned by the disease. At any one time it caters for around fifty girls and boys ranging in age from six months to eighteen years. Sherlene was already supporting the orphanage financially when she read about Bees Abroad in a beekeeping magazine Down Under and approached us with the idea of organising a project that would not only provide extra nutrition for the orphans and staff while possibly generating a little bit of income for the orphanage through the sale of any surplus honey, but which would also serve as a training facility for the older children that would enable them to leave with a skill that might help them to make a living for themselves when the time came for them to move out.

The accommodation we were offered at the Centre was, not surprisingly, much more basic than that provided at Egerton. We were allocated rooms in a dilapidated brick building with broken glass in the windows, doors that didn't quite fit the frames, no electric lights and no running water. The room Mary and I shared had two single beds with one-inch-thick mattresses and just one mosquito net between the two of us. We decided we would probably be better off if we put both mattresses onto one bed and squeezed into it together under the single mosquito net. Having retired on the first night, we had just about managed to get ourselves settled within the narrow confines of the bed when Mary suddenly froze and squealed: "John, there's something in the room! It just jumped onto the bed and walked across my legs!"

It was pitch black, there was no light of any kind and I'd forgotten to unpack our torch and to have it ready beside the bed for just such an

25

emergency. As I nervously slid out from under the mosquito net, felt for our suitcase and started rummaging around for the torch there was a sudden movement and whatever it was shot across the room, leapt through the empty window frame and was gone.

With my heart thumping I grabbed the plastic washing-up bowl that served as a wash basin, jammed it into the window frame and strapped it in with my belt. Mary and I were both like a bag of nerves by his time and it was a while before either of us started to drop off again and then suddenly we were wide awake once more as Mary screamed: "It's there again! I felt it on my leg!"

"Calm down and don't panic," I whispered, explaining reassuringly that this time there was nothing there to be afraid of – that what she had felt was just my arm falling across her as I tried to get comfortable.

We eventually dozed off and managed to sleep fitfully until early the next morning when we were awoken by the sounds of the women getting a fire lit outside and boiling up a cauldron of ugali, the maize porridge that is their staple diet. There was then a knock on the door and a bucket of cold water was left for us to wash with. Luckily, we had brought a good stock of wipes with us! As for the toilets, which were located some distance away from the house, they were of what I think can most accurately be described as the squat-and-drop variety – definitely not for those of a sensitive disposition! However, the friendliness of our hosts, their obvious gratitude and enthusiasm for what we were trying to do for them and the satisfaction we got from knowing that it was all so worthwhile, combined with the sense of adventure, more than made up for most of the discomforts. And we were rather humbled when we discovered later that the house we were in was home to some of the orphanage staff who had been turfed out to make way for us. By their standards, almost any brick building was considered the height of luxury.

Our story of the mysterious night-time intruder was greeted with stifled amusement by our hosts who giggled among themselves and assured us that it was almost certainly nothing more threatening than a feral cat, one of several that lived around the orphanage, helping to keep the rodent population under control. This was not our only slightly disconcerting wildlife encounter while we were in residence. The following day a small

David and Gillian Asiago
with orphans at the
Maranatha Family Centre

black snake was spotted slithering into the house before disappearing down a hole in a corner of one room. This caused much excitement and water was poured down the hole in a vain effort to drive it out. When this failed, the hole was covered over. We were anxious that the snake might pop up somewhere else but were again assured that there was nothing to worry about, that it was a completely harmless variety. I don't think any of us were totally convinced and from then on there was much peering under beds and shaking out of boots.

Pam and I had arranged to give a brief introductory beekeeping course, which was attended by a dozen of the orphanage staff. We armed them with notebooks, pencils and simple guide books and I then went through all the basics before going on to give a demonstration of how to build a top bar hive. The whole class came with us into town to help us buy the necessary materials, including wood, a saw, a hammer and some nails. The total cost was £20, paid out of our Bees Abroad cash float. When we got back it emerged that arrangements had been made for a local carpenter to come and actually put the hive together because, as teachers themselves, the trainees regarded that sort of manual work as being beneath them! At that point I threw a wobbly and insisted that they had to do it themselves if they were going to learn anything and be able to pass it on. I got them to tell the carpenter that his services would not be required after all as there was no money to pay him, but, being smart, he stayed on anyway to see how it was done, realising that he might in future be able to make hives and sell them if the beekeeping really took off!

Having completed the hive we then went in search of a suitable site in which to set it up. This involved a walk of what seemed like several miles to a spot which I had been assured would be ideal. And it was. It was in a little spinney, just off the beaten track and therefore safe and secure from curious passers-by. There was shade under the trees, a mixture of crops nearby, including coffee bushes, and also plenty of water in the vicinity. Pam and I agreed that this would do very nicely. The hive was set up and baited and, much to everyone's delight, was soon occupied. A good start.

As at Nessuit, Mary discussed healthcare issues with the women involved in the project while Pam Gregory demonstrated how to make candles from beeswax, using cotton strands from a mophead as wicks, and also cosmetics such as a basic barrier cream that is produced by mixing beeswax and the local margarine – very good for babies' sore bottoms, I was reliably informed! Partly, perhaps, because of the African culture, these woman-to-woman sessions seemed to work especially well, the local wives, mothers and their daughters finding it much easier to discuss such matters with a fellow female.

Mary talking to members of the women's group at Nessuit

After a few days, having completed our work at the orphanage, we headed north for Eldoret, where Dr Reuben Muasya, Dean of Agriculture at Moi University, had invited Pam and me to speak to the staff and students about the benefits of beekeeping not just as a source of food and possibly income but also as a means of boosting crop pollination.

This invitation had come as the result of a chance meeting with Dr Muasya at the Royal Show at Stoneleigh in Warwickshire. He had wandered into the beekeeping tent where Mary was serving up honey ice cream and when she noticed from his overseas visitor accreditation badge that he was from Kenya she told him that she was sure I would like to meet him as I was about to go out there on behalf of Bees Abroad. She explained that I had had to pop out of the tent for a few minutes, gave him an ice cream and asked if he would hang around for a few minutes until I returned, which he did. We then had a long chat about what Bees Abroad was planning to do in Kenya at the end of which he made me promise to come and visit him at the university while I was in the country.

Introducing us to the staff and students there he made a point of saying how much he had appreciated the way in which Mary had made him feel welcome at the Royal Show. He recalled how lonely and out of place he had always felt when he was doing his agricultural training in Europe as a young man and how refreshing it was to be offered the hand of friendship by someone who seemed genuinely interested in who he was and what he was doing.

Our journey from the orphanage to Eldoret had started with a short matatu ride to Kisii, a few miles down the road. Mary had a pretty hefty hold-all and was amazed when the very slender wife of Moses, one of the two managers at the orphanage, picked it up effortlessly, popped it on top of her head and marched off with it to the matatu pick-up point as if it weighed nothing at all.

It was the early morning rush hour and as we tried to get aboard the packed matatu into town it was like finding yourself caught in a rugby scrum, with everybody pushing forward and cramming themselves into the little minibus. We didn't actually see our bags come aboard but just assumed that they had been stowed on the roof.

At Kisii we boarded another matatu bound for Eldoret, a 100-mile journey that took the best part of a day and involved the usual heart-in-the-mouth moments as well as some breath-taking scenery. When we eventually arrived at our destination we were pleasantly surprised to find that we had been booked into an old colonial hotel in the centre of town – a bit dog-eared, but positively five-star compared to anything we'd had up until then.

The next morning we were picked up at the hotel and taken to the university to meet the Principal and his staff before Pam and I then gave a two-hour presentation. This was well-received and, as ever on these occasions, we were impressed by the thirst for knowledge shown by the students and the intensity of their desire to learn from us. Afterwards, during lunch with the staff and some of the students, there was much enthusiastic talk of setting up a beekeeping training and demonstration unit at the university, with input from Bees Abroad.

After lunch we were taken on a tour of the university farm during which I was impressed to learn, among other things, that all the animal waste from the farm was harvested and converted into methane gas that was then used to fuel the university's entire cooking requirements, a model example of environment-friendly recycling.

The following day, Pam, John, Mary and I went our separate ways – Pam and John braving the road to hell to go and visit a proposed Bees Abroad project at Kissoro in Uganda while Mary and I headed to Mombasa, via Nairobi, for a week's break and a chance to recoup and to reflect on our experiences.

Refreshed and re-energised after this welcome break we then returned to Nairobi where we met up with Roger Molera, founder and director of Wings of Mercy, a community-based charity organisation working in the slums and shanty towns in and around the capital. Beekeeping would obviously not be practical in the slums themselves but Molera's idea was that by creating employment and generating income in the surrounding villages it might be possible to slow down the drift to Nairobi of young people who, when their dreams of finding a better life for themselves in the city almost inevitably failed to work out, finished up in the slums, worsening the already appalling conditions there and adding to health problems, primarily the spread of HIV/AIDS.

We suggested to Roger that Wings of Mercy should prepare a comprehensive project proposal and submit it to Bees Abroad, which he readily agreed to do. Meanwhile, arrangements were made to take us the next day to an area around Machakos, some two hours' drive south of Nairobi, to assess the overall potential for such a project. The locality certainly looked promising, with a number of hives already in existence, and Bees Abroad has since gone on to support the project, raising funds to send six prospective group leaders to the National Beekeeping Station in Nairobi for training and providing them with five hives each to set up as demonstration and training apiaries. At the last count there was a total of almost a hundred beekeepers in two separate groups, with well over fifty hives between them. Both groups have benefited from the training that we provided on a subsequent visit and also from that given by David Njuguna, an experienced Kenyan beekeeping trainer with whom Bees Abroad has come to work very closely.

A very likeable man in his mid-fifties, David is a jovial character who gets on well with everybody he meets and who certainly knows his stuff when it comes to beekeeping, having written and printed out his own basic manual. He effectively works for us as a part-time volunteer, being paid little more than the out-of-pocket travel expenses he incurs in regularly visiting our various projects from his home near Mount Kenya in his spare time, keeping an eye on them and giving advice wherever and whenever necessary. It helps enormously to have someone local on the ground keeping us in touch with what is going on and if we can raise sufficient sponsorship funds we would like to be able to retain his services.

Bees Abroad's voluntary in-country trainer David Njuguna (centre, in green shirt)

The final highlight of that initial trip to Kenya was a day spent with Peter Paterson. Well-known internationally as well as throughout Africa, where he has devoted his entire life to beekeeping development, Peter has written extensively on the subject. We had got an introduction through a friend of

Great hats think alike! Me with renowned Kenyan beekeeper Peter Paterson

our daughter whose parents knew the Paterson family very well. Apart from that, Peter was already aware of Bees Abroad and what we were trying to do and was therefore only too happy to meet us.

He turned out to be a real gentleman in every sense. He came personally to collect us from our bed-and-breakfast accommodation in Nairobi in a rather ancient but immaculate Humber-type car and then drove us out to his home, a beautiful old colonial-style house just outside the capital. It was fascinating to talk to him and to gain the benefit of his extensive practical knowledge and experience of beekeeping in Africa. He led us on a tour of his grounds, where he has many different types of hives set up, and then invited us to taste the various types of honey he had stored in his kitchen. Until then, the only African honeys I had tasted were all dark, strong and aromatic, even slightly smokey. But he had some that were very light-coloured with a beautiful perfume to them.

As we left, he presented us with a copy of the newly-published book on beekeeping that he had written for the MacMillan series Tropical Agriculture and we bought six more copies to give to friends as presents. It was the perfect end to a trip that had made a deep and lasting impression on both Mary and me and which left us more committed than ever to Bees Abroad.

There was an interesting little postscript to our visit. Our chamber maid at the Kwality Inn, where we stayed in Nairobi, was a quiet, very shy and rather sad-looking young woman named Rose. We were determined to make her smile before we left and eventually succeeded on our last day when we handed her what, by local standards, was a pretty hefty tip, amounting to about £10. Her older sister emailed us later to thank us on Rose's behalf and to say how much our kindness had been appreciated.

Sadly, we got another email a few months later telling us that Rose had been sacked from her job at the hotel as a result of accidentally losing some room keys, on top of which she had also been docked a month's wages to pay for the replacement of the locks. She wanted to know if she could come and work for us in England as our housekeeper. We replied explaining that unfortunately this would not be possible but, desperately wanting to do something to help, sent her some cross-stitch patterns along with a couple of teach yourself instruction books in the hope that this might enable her to learn a skill that would earn her a bit of pin money. She succeeded in doing just that, producing some beautiful work, a few examples of which we were able to sell for her over here. One friend of ours who saw some of what she had done was so impressed that she sent her a whole load of materials to work with.

Meanwhile, it had further transpired that Rose was a single mother with a daughter, Yvonne, who was having to live with another of Rose's sisters in Mombasa. When we heard about this we offered to sponsor her to go to school. Since then we've received regular progress reports and it turns out that Yvonne is as bright as a button, up there at the top of the class and doing well.

There are so many problems in Africa and so many people who are desperately in need of help. What we, as individuals, were able to do in this instance amounted to no more than the tiniest drop in the ocean, but at least we have the satisfaction of knowing that we've been able to improve the lot of one little girl and her mother. It is to be hoped that as time goes on a great many more will benefit from Bees Abroad's mission.

3: Travels with my Granddaughter

Africa today is seen as a continent in crisis and all too often outside efforts to help alleviate poverty, starvation and disease and to aid development in the poorest of its countries are undermined by political instability, a culture of corruption among government officials at every level and fierce, deep-seated tribal divisions. Kenya had been enjoying a period of relative calm until the disputed Presidential election of December 2007 sparked an outbreak of widespread and often violent unrest throughout the country, prompting the Foreign Office to advise British nationals against going there.

Some of the worst violence was concentrated in the area around Nakuru and Kisii, where the Maranatha Family Centre orphanage suffered a particularly savage attack during which six of the older girls were raped by a rampaging gang while manager David Asiago and his wife, Gillian, were badly beaten up as they tried to protect the girls, one of whom died of her injuries. The raiders also stole a computer and a generator.

Not surprisingly, the beekeeping project was put on hold while David and his team at the Centre got back on their feet again once order had been restored nationally with the brokering in early 2008 of a power-sharing deal between presidential rivals Mwai Kibaki and Raila Odinga. With continued funding from Sherlene Turner to pay for training and hive-making, along with further back-up from Bees Abroad, it soon picked up again, going from strength to strength over the next few months so that by the time I went back in late 2008 there were twenty hives on three different sites. Between them, these hives were already producing enough honey to satisfy the needs of the Centre, plus a healthy surplus for sale to outsiders, thereby generating much needed extra income.

A policy had also been introduced whereby every boy, when he left the

Gillian and David Asiago and (centre) their baby son, in the arms of an aunty

Members of a Kerio Valley women's group model protective suits made from maize bags.

orphanage at the age of eighteen, was to be given a hive with which to start his own beekeeping enterprise, the first two leavers having already been sent on their way with hives as farewell gifts. The girls, meanwhile, were all learning how to make protective beekeeper clothing out of discarded food aid maize sacks and old mosquito nets, using patterns supplied by Pam Gregory. They were running them up on an ancient Singer sewing machine that they also used to make their own dresses. Being rather scratchy, a bit like a hair shirt, the sacking is not very comfortable but it does the job adequately while the mozzie nets make efficient honey filters as well as face masks.

I actually made two trips to Kenya during the course of 2008. I went first in March to attend a three-day meeting of ApiTrade Africa, a newly-established honey trade network set up in 2007 to represent producers and to promote beekeeping throughout the continent. The meeting had originally been scheduled for January but had to be postponed because of the troubles.

While I was there, I took the opportunity to visit the National Beekeeping Station, a government facility set up as part of Kenya's Ministry of Livestock and Fisheries Development. Located in Karen, a rather posh old colonial suburb of Nairobi named after *Out of Africa* author Karen Blixen, this turned out to be a slightly down-at-heel but nevertheless rather lovely little establishment where a dedicated and enthusiastic staff led by a wonderful character named Robin Mbae were working hard to promote beekeeping throughout the country, hosting educational tours for farmers, university students and schoolchildren and providing basic training courses for would-be beekeepers and the ministry's own district field officers.

As well as a classroom, a rudimentary dormitory set-up, a sparsely-equipped laboratory and a small, thinly-stocked library, facilities include demonstration sites featuring various different types of hive along with a timber workshop where hive-making can be taught. Included among the full-time staff of twenty-five are both a tailor, to teach the making of protective clothing, and a tinsmith, to demonstrate the making of simple smokers. There is also a little shop that sells honey and various beeswax products.

Up to 150 farmers every year attend the Station's one-week residential training courses while many more come on one-day educational visits during which they are given a general introduction to all aspects of apiculture. Given the constraints of the shoestring budget within which they have to operate, I was impressed with the level of success achieved by Robin Mbae and his team, which included another charming character named Blaise Okinyi, who had translated Pam's basic beekeeping manual into Swahili after meeting her on a beekeeping course in Belgium.

During my short stay in Nairobi I also went out to Machakos to see what progress had been made with the Wings of Mercy project there. Among other things, I was taken to see a basic tailoring workshop that had been set up in another Nairobi slum area and it occurred to me that they might be able to make basic protective beekeeping clothing there. Back in England, Mary set about persuading people to donate any surplus or unwanted sewing equipment to be sent out to them. We approached local churches and organisations and also made a point of mentioning it in the talks and presentations that we do from time to time. Before long we had amassed quite a collection of cotton, wool, fabrics, zips, patterns, buttons, Velcro, needles, pins and pinking scissors. A friend who worked for FedEx then very kindly used his personal discount allowance to send a consignment out to Kenya and since then Mary and I have taken as much as can pack into our hand luggage each time we go out there. As it happens, they never did get to make protective clothing for various reasons, but we continued to support what remains a hugely worthwhile venture.

 36

Mary and I were back in August that same year, accompanied this time by our sixteen-year-old granddaughter, Becky. We paid for her to join us for the first two weeks of our month-long visit, thinking it would be an exciting and educational adventure for her. Our itinerary on this occasion included not only visits to Nessuit, Machakos and the Maranatha Family Centre but also assessments of two potential new projects.

The location for the first of these was up in the north west of the country in the Cheringani Hills near Kitale. Here, a well-run organisation calling itself the Sustainable Mobilisation of Agricultural Resource Technologies (SMART) was engaged in providing help, advice and training for subsistence farmers in an area where a large population was putting the natural resources and the environment under considerable pressure. In particular, there was concern about the depletion of the forest through charcoal burning. SMART had been set up with the aim of encouraging various more sustainable alternatives, including the growing of crops other than maize along with a range of organic vegetables, with an emphasis on improved and drought-resistant varieties. The introduction of dairy goat-herding having proved to be a popular and successful initiative, beekeeping was seen as another very promising possibility, which was why Bees Abroad had been approached for help and support.

To save time – and, again, at our own expense – we decided that rather than going by road we would fly up to Kitale, taking off from Nairobi's domestic Wilson Airport in a 20-seater light aircraft. The sensation was a bit like being in an Austin Seven with wings, but I actually felt a lot safer than I often did in a matatu, even when the pilot was ducking and diving in order to avoid the occasional thunderstorms we encountered along the way. And the views, looking down on the vast expanse of Africa, were breathtaking.

However, this genuinely was a no-frills airline. When we landed on the airstrip at Kitale we were simply dumped unceremoniously on the runway along with our suitcases. Fortunately, project leader Jack Wafula was there to meet us and drive us into town, where we had been booked into a small hotel located above a parade of shops. It didn't look much from outside, but the rooms were adequate and the staff friendly, especially the dining room waiters on whom Becky instantly made a big impression! In fact, she turned

Granddaughter Becky became the centre of attention wherever we went

out to be the centre of attention wherever we went during our stay.

The next morning we were collected and driven out to the project headquarters where Jack introduced us to his three full-time field officers – his wife Everlyn, Ms Eunice Wamboi and Mr Dismas Marango. All three had studied at the local Manor House Agricultural Centre, while Jack himself also had an American qualification in Biointensive Agriculture plus nine years experience working with organisations that specialised in promoting sustainable agricultural development.

I was immediately impressed by what was clearly a very well-run organisation. The way it worked was that Everlyn, Eunice and Dismas between them were responsible for five separate groups of between thirty and fifty members, mostly women and young people. These groups were scattered around the Cheringani Hills, about an hour's drive from Kitale, and each of the field officers was supplied with a small motorbike, making it possible for them to travel around between the groups in their charge on a regular basis. Each group had its own vegetable plot for practical educational purposes and in return for a modest membership fee the members were supplied with seeds and plants as well as expert training and general support. There were regular monthly meetings of the field officers and detailed quarterly reports on the progress of each group.

A guided tour of the area revealed plenty of evidence of traditional beekeeping, with a number of log hives spotted hanging from trees, mostly alongside water courses, a further clear indication that this was a bee-friendly environment.

Having been shown around, I had no hesitation in recommending that this should be our next project in Kenya, providing that a sponsor could be found to fund it. The proposal that I eventually put forward for approval allowed for total expenditure of £16,000 over an initial three-year period. That money would go towards paying for the organisation of training and hive-making workshops for the five groups, the setting up of three demonstration apiaries (including hives, smokers and protective clothing), the supply of harvesting equipment (including bottles, cartons and labels) and the setting up of a micro-credit scheme to provide finance for hive-making. A sum of £5,000 was also set aside to pay the accommodation, living and travel expenses for David Njuguna to spend six months of each year at Kitale overseeing the project.

Unfortunately, at the time of writing we have still been unable to find a sponsor, so our full involvement in the project is on hold. In the meantime, however, a donation of £1,000 from a company that makes beekeeping equipment in the UK has been used to finance further training of the field officers by me and William Arusei, a local Kenyan beekeeping trainer attached to an organisation called SITE. SITE is part of Tradecraft and promotes beekeeping under the banner BELIEVE – Beekeeping as a Livelihood in Extremely Vulnerable Environments. Bees Abroad has also paid for the purchase of various items of equipment and we remain hopeful that a suitable funder will eventually be found so that we can implement the full development plan.

While in Kitale we also managed to fit in an unscheduled visit to a beekeeping enterprise in a village not far away that had been started by a man called Peter Otengo, whom I had met some months earlier at an international beekeeping convention in Australia.

Peter came with an old school friend of his to collect us from our hotel and drove us up to the village, where he had built a little training centre. He was keeping the bees in clay pots some distance from the village and I was keen to get a photograph of him and his friend standing next to them. As it happened, there was a storm brewing at the time, the air pressure was heavy and in such conditions bees can be a bit twitchy, especially the more aggressive African varieties. The flash on my camera obviously aggravated them even further, provoking them into a mass attack. We all ran for it, but while Peter and his friend stayed in the open and were caught and stung several times I dived straight into a field of maize that was taller than I am and, weaving in and out, soon lost my pursuers and eventually emerged unscathed.

But that was by no means the end of the day's drama. By the time the three of us had reconvened rather breathlessly at the top of the field the storm was about to break. We started hurrying back towards the village but had not gone very far when the heavens opened. There was no way we were going to get all the way back to Peter's place without getting soaked to the skin so we simply made a dash for the first house we came to and asked if we could shelter there. We were welcomed inside with great enthusiasm and introduced to the whole family while outside this huge storm raged, the sound of torrential rain hammering down on the corrugated iron roof of the house rising to such a deafening crescendo that it was almost impossible to hear yourself speak.

When the deluge finally abated we said farewell to our impromptu hosts and went on down to see the training classroom that Peter had built with money from a Danish charity. It soon became clear why he had been so keen to get me up there. He had added a bit of accommodation on one side of the classroom but by some extraordinary chance this had been occupied by what was undoubtedly the biggest natural swarm of bees that I had ever seen. What Peter wanted was for me to show him how to get them into the hives.

The largest natural swarm I have ever seen – snapping this picture almost literally stirred up a hornets' nest

What happened next merely showed that none of us had learned any lessons from our earlier encounter with the colony in the clay pots. I was determined to get a picture of this giant swarm but once again the flash stirred the bees up and we had to beat a very hasty retreat, scurrying down the concrete steps to get away. And just as before, Peter and his friend made the mistake of running across open ground, with the angry bees in hot pursuit, while I dodged around the corner into a half-built building and hid in a dark corner whereupon the bees that were chasing me abandoned their attack and headed back to the light, which they will always tend to do.

We eventually got back to Peter's house to find that the jungle drums had been beating and word of my presence had got around, with the result that everybody in the vicinity with an interest in beekeeping had arrived on the scene, expecting me to give an impromptu lecture on the subject. They listened intently as I explained to Peter how I thought he might be able to divide up the colony in the training centre and get them into several different hives. But I knew it wasn't going to be easy. It would have been a challenge even for me, with all my experience. I never got to hear whether or not he managed it. Next time I'm in Kitale I'll have to look him up and find out what happened. .

From Kitale, Mary, Becky and I travelled some fifty miles south to the Kerio Valley, just east of Eldoret, to assess another possible project that had been put forward by an organisation known by the acronym EMEDEN, standing for Empower, Mentor and Develop. Run by a formidable lady named Everlyne Cherobon, EMEDEN is committed to improving the lot of smallholders in Kenya's poorest and most deprived rural areas, of which the Kerio Valley is a prime example.

Located at the northern end of the Rift Valley, it is semi-arid, largely forested and features a hilly, rocky terrain that makes is unsuitable for many forms of traditional farming. At one time fluorspar mining provided employment in the region but the mines have mostly been worked out and abandoned now and people mostly survive on very small-scale subsistence farming together with various hunting activities. The felling of trees for charcoal burning and to clear space for crop cultivation is causing environmental damage.

Making traditional log hives in the
Kerio Valley

Traditional bark hives hanging in the
trees in Kenya

However, conditions there do indeed favour beekeeping thanks to the combination of a warm climate, two distinct rainy seasons and the existence of three types of nectar-bearing acacia trees that flower in succession, providing a long, continuous honey flow. And, in fact, there is a long tradition of beekeeping, with log and bark hives suspended high in the trees.

I was told that there were probably thousands of such hives throughout the valley, but that beekeeping was the exclusive preserve of the men, who used most of the honey to make honey beer – an alcoholic brew that is not much to European tastes and certainly wouldn't win any awards from the Campaign for Real Ale! As a result, there was no nutritional benefit or income for the men's families.

With an ever-increasing number of women-led households as a result of HIV/AIDS, EMEDEN were keen to challenge this traditional men-only approach and to establish beekeeping as a profitable and sustainable economic activity, with families undertaking hive management to produce both nutrition and income. They had already made a start on this, with five groups having been set up.

Having had a chance to look around the area and meet those group members who had already been recruited, I had no doubt that the scheme had the potential to benefit hundreds of families in the valley and I recommended that Bees Abroad should get involved.

During our stay there, Everlyne had arranged accommodation for us in a local safari lodge, which was very comfortable Over the next two days we were taken out in a typical old banger of a car to visit the five groups and it wasn't long before Becky was introduced to the hazards of road travel in rural Africa.

On the second morning Everlyne didn't turn up on time and when she and her driver did eventually arrive it turned out that the car was playing up. It seemed the fan wasn't cutting in, causing the engine to overheat and making it necessary to keep stopping every few miles to let it cool down and then topping the radiator up with water. When we got to the first place on the day's itinerary the driver took it off to a local repair garage to be looked at while I was meeting the members of the group and making a brief presentation. This was followed by lunch, a traditional Kenyan meal that consisted of all sorts of different things served up on a wooden board, not all of them immediately identifiable!

Our driver had meanwhile returned with both good news and bad news. The bad news was that the car could not be repaired until a vital spare part could be fetched from Eldoret. The good news was that the garage owner had agreed to loan him a battered Subaru estate as a temporary replacement until the part arrived. We all piled gratefully into the Subaru only to realise before we had gone very far that it was desperately low on fuel in an area where petrol stations are very few and far between.

We were still a little way from our next destination when the driver resorted to the usual practice of swinging the car from side to side to milk the last drop of fuel from the tank. This had the side-effect of causing a strange creaking noise from the rear of the vehicle. The source of this noise was revealed when, just as we pulled up at the place where we were to meet the next group, there was a horrible clunk and the back wheel fell off! Once again, the driver promised he would get it fixed while I was making my presentation and we left him jacking the car up on stones.

Once finished there, we were due to drive straight to the airport at Eldoret, from where we had a flight booked back to Nairobi. So, given that we now had a car with a missing back wheel and no petrol, we were understandably a little apprehensive. However, by the time we were ready to leave a couple of hours later the wheel was back on and there was petrol in the tank.

Our relief was short-lived. We hadn't gone a mile down the road before there was another loud clunk and the wheel fell off again. This was serious. We were now stuck in the middle of nowhere, with the sun beating down, no means of transport and the minutes fast ticking away before we were due at the airport. Thank goodness for mobile phones. A call to the garage where the original car was being repaired established that it was nearly ready and it was agreed that it would be driven out to where we were stranded. After an anxious, nail-biting wait, during which we kept checking our watches with mounting concern, it eventually arrived about an hour later. There was then a heated discussion between Everlyne and the mechanic about how much it was going to cost before we were finally able to get on our way again.

Our driver shifted enthusiastically into rally mode and we roared up out of the valley on a very steep, badly potholed road. How we got to the top in one piece I'll never quite know. We then tore through the rush hour traffic into Eldoret, arriving at the airport just in time to see our plane taking off! With Becky due to fly back to England from Nairobi ahead of us the next morning we had no option but to fork out for a flight on another airline, but were just thankful that we were able to grab the last three seats available.

Becky had to return to England before us in order to get back in time for the start of the new school year. As with most people going to Africa for the first time she had been shocked by the level of poverty she encountered but, at the same time, had also been impressed by the friendliness of the people and the cheerfulness they exuded despite the often desperate circumstances in which they had to struggle for survival. And she coped very well with the rather basic accommodation and toilet facilities we occasionally encountered along the way.

The whole experience was also to stand her in very good stead when she returned to Africa two years later with a party of staff and sixth formers from her school on an annual exchange visit to the school in Uganda with which her school is twinned. She was better prepared than anyone.

Having put Becky on her flight home, Mary and I went up to Nessuit to see how things were getting on there before then moving on to Sondhu to visit a school whose rural science department was thinking of setting up a beekeeping project partly as an educational facility. The school was twinned with one in Wem, Shropshire that was considering the possibility of helping to fund the project and I had been asked to go and have a look and report back on its feasibility.

We stayed with the headmaster in his house, a bungalow that had internal walls but no ceilings, with the result that there was a rather disconcerting lack of total privacy since you could hear quite clearly what was going on elsewhere in the building. We were awoken abruptly at daybreak the next morning when a monkey jumped out of a tree onto the tin roof of a dog kennel. This started the dogs barking, which in turn set the chickens off and soon it was complete bedlam. Outside our bedroom door was a bucket of warm water with which to wash and flush the toilet.

While we there, the headmaster drove us out to look at an impressively large irrigation dam that had been built by the Japanese. On the way back he suddenly and unexpectedly announced: "I think we should go to the pub for a drink." A few miles up the road he stopped in a little village that comprised no more than a few shacks. Leading us up to one of them he told us: "There are two pubs in the village but this is the one I prefer" and proceeded to hammer loudly on the closed door. The owner eventually appeared and rather reluctantly opened up, took the shutters off the windows and put a light on behind the makeshift bar. We were then offered the choice of a soft drink or a beer. Mary opted for a fizzy soft drink while I and the headmaster had a bottle of beer each which we drank in the otherwise deserted 'pub', clearly the sort of rural drinking den that only usually opened at night. The headmaster had been on an exchange visit to the school at Wem and with hindsight I suspect that he had somehow got the idea then that going to the pub was the done thing as far as the English were concerned. It was a rather amusing little interlude.

I again put in a report in favour of the project but heard nothing back from Wem until quite some time later when I was told that they had unfortunately had second thoughts about getting involved because of misgivings about the true educational value of the proposed investment.

It was after we left Sondhu that we made our return visit to the orphanage at Gucca, where we were delighted to see how well they had managed to recover from the devastating attack just eight months earlier, thanks largely

45

to the commitment of David and Gillian Asiago, Moses and the rest of the team there.

From Gucca it was back to Nairobi to catch the flight home. Our trip had ended on a very positive note; and with what looked like very promising new projects in Kitale and the Kerio Valley I felt that Bees Abroad was making its mark in Kenya. And although it has been disappointing not to be able to find the full funding required to finance the proposed development at Kitale, Kerio Valley has benefited from an unexpectedly valuable windfall.

This came about as a result of a special charity fun run organised by the Trevor-Roberts School, a North London prep school founded by a former private tutor to the Prince of Wales. The run is an annual event, but to tie in with the 2010 general election it was decided that individual pupils should each put forward their chosen charity as a candidate to receive all the money raised and that after these had been narrowed down to a shortlist of four there would then be an 'election' campaign, complete with booths in the playground, at the end of which votes would be cast to pick the most deserving charity.

Bees Abroad was represented by nine-year-old Archie Blair (no relation to the former PM!), whose father had found out about us on the Internet and thought that with all the concern about a crisis threatening the British bee population we would be a good topical candidate.

As part of his campaign, young Archie got in touch with us and asked if we could send someone down to speak to the school about the work we did and I agreed to go along. I first met headmaster Simon Trevor-Roberts, the son of the founder, who welcomed me with a large schooner of sherry and asked me all about Bees Abroad before taking me on a tour of the school, which had fantastic facilities. After lunch with the pupils and staff I then gave my talk and answered a lot of very intelligent questions from the floor. As I left, I presented Archie with a jar of Fosse Way honey.

We had been told in advance that the run was expected to raise about £1800 so we were overjoyed when the school rang to say that Archie had won the election for us, inviting us to send someone along to pick up the cheque at the end of term Speech Day. As I was going to be away that day Claire Waring went in my place.

Me with Archie Blair
and headmaster Simon
Trevor-Roberts, son of
the school's founder

When I got home there was a near hysterical message from Claire waiting for me on my answer phone. "John! John! I've had the most amazing day at the school. But we didn't get the £1800 after all." There was then a pause before she added: "We got £5,500!"

I immediately rang our administrator, Veronica Brown, on her mobile to pass on the good news. Veronica's husband is a scout leader and she was helping him to set up a cub camp in Malvern at the time. When I told her how much we had actually received she let out a squeal of delight. "That'll set me up for the weekend," she told me. "I can now deal with any little brat that likes to try it on with me!"

4: Getting the Buzz

The earliest beginnings of my career as a beekeeper can be traced back to the moment one Sunday morning when my younger sister, Jan, burst into the kitchen of the family home in Clifton, Bristol, her face screwed up in disgust, and shouted: "There's something really weird out here in the garden – come and have a look!" I followed her out and there, hanging from the branch of a small tree, was a swarm of honey bees the size of a rugby ball. My eyes lit up; I knew exactly what needed to be done.

I had already left home by this time and was working as an assistant to John Henry Dunkley, farm manager at the Gloucestershire Farm Institute at Hartpury, now known as Hartpury College, a job I had been offered after completing an agricultural training course at the Institute. This had all come about by chance rather than design. There was no tradition of farming anywhere in my family background. My father, Harold, was the manager of a shoe shop in Bristol – one of a small family-owned chain called Goodenough's – and, until she got married, my mother, Edna, used to work behind the counter in a sweetshop.

At secondary modern school the only subject for which I showed any real aptitude was woodwork. Apart from that, my main interest was in sport, mainly rugby and cross-country running. I had absolutely no idea what I wanted to do when I left school and drifted into farming after being offered a job as a labourer on a farm at Tickenham, near Clevedon.

From there I moved on to a bigger farm on the outskirts of Bristol, part of the Hollywood Tower estate that was owned by local industrial magnate Sir George Stanley White. Sir George is best remembered as the owner of the Bristol Aircraft Company – which built the Brabazon – and the Bristol Bus Company. He was also a leading figure in the Bristol and Clifton Zoological Society, owners of Bristol Zoo. In fact, Home Farm, along with the rest of the estate, was later taken over by the zoo and developed into a wildlife park.

 48

Me as a schoolboy with my parents, Harold and Edna, and sister Jannette

A swarm like the one that alarmed my sister

It was the farm manager at Home Farm, Mr Downs, who encouraged me to go to agricultural college, telling me that if I was going to stay in farming I needed to get some sort of specialist qualification, otherwise I was never likely to be anything more than a labourer. So I applied to the Farm Institute, which was run by Gloucester County Council, and was accepted for the General Agriculture course. The Council gave me a grant to cover my tuition fees but it wasn't until I actually went to enrol that I discovered that the grant didn't cover my accommodation and there was a moment of panic until my parents, who could ill afford it, agreed to cover the extra cost. When I was then retained to work on the college farm, having completed the one-year course and gained a National Certificate in Agriculture, my accommodation was provided free as part of the deal, but I would regularly go back to Bristol at weekends for all the usual reasons – to get my washing done and to enjoy a bit of decent home cooking!

As was the case at most agricultural colleges in those days, basic beekeeping was included as part of the core syllabus at Hartpury, where it was taught by one Harrison Ashforth. Harry, as he was better known to everyone except the readers of his regular column in the *British Bee Journal*, was also in charge of the college's poultry section and had a favourite little joke that he delighted in telling each new intake of students. "A queen bee produces between 2,000 and 3,000 eggs-a-day," he would say, adding with a

College days - with the soccer team (front, left), with all the students and staff (see if you can spot me in the back row) and on my last day, smartly dressed for the end-of-year ball

chuckle: "Just think what a fortune you could make if you could only find a way of transplanting that bee gene into hens!"

Harry certainly never made a fortune but he did manage to augment his college income with a couple of lucrative sidelines. As well as a hatchery from which he sold day-old chicks hatched from fertile eggs produced by the college farm's hens he also had around two hundred of his own bee hives sited on farms around the Cotswolds, each producing between 60-100lbs of honey. He needed some part-time labouring help in running these two enterprises and I was only too happy to oblige, grateful for the extra pocket money I earned from working for him in the evenings and at weekends. In addition, I gained a great deal of what was to prove very valuable practical experience of beekeeping on top of what I had been taught in the classroom. Not that the idea of making a career out of commercial beekeeping had ever occurred to me at this stage. I was just thinking of it as something I might do on the side, a hobby out of which I might also be able to make a few bob. It was the swarm that turned up in my parents' back garden that Sunday morning that got me started.

I didn't have any proper equipment with me, of course, but with an old net curtain draped over my head for protection I used a pair of secateurs

50

to snip the branch and gently lowered the swarm into a tea chest that I had found lying around at the back of our garden shed. I then wrapped the net curtain around the chest and took the whole lot back to Hartpury on the back seat of the ancient Austin 10 that was one of the first things I had bought out of the wages I had saved up.

Harry very kindly gave me one of his hives and permission to site it in the college grounds. Unfortunately, the first site I picked turned out to be too near the bike sheds and when students started complaining about being stung I had to move the hive to a spot on the college farm, less than a mile away. This was another elementary mistake. I didn't move it far enough and when the bees went foraging their natural homing instinct was confused, still partly locked onto the original site. The students were still getting stung and I was losing my foraging bees. My solution to this problem was to place an empty box at the original site and then, every evening at dusk, I would take those bees that had collected there, carry them to the new site in the box and throw them into the top of the hive until, after two or three days, they eventually got the message.

Me (second left) helping farm manager John Henry Dunkley (far left) with the harvest on the college farm at Hartpury

Over the next few months, with encouragement from Harry, I added two more hives, which I paid for by selling honey to the students. I still have the receipt from local Bristol beekeeper C.J. Reynolds showing that for a new National hive, complete with brood box and a set of new brood combs, he charged me just £3. Happy days! You would now expect to pay at least £300 for the same sort of kit.

Unfortunately, I then lost my job at the college after falling out with the Principal and the Bursar as a result of a dispute over accommodation. Three of us staff assistants had been sharing a rather nice flat on the campus but it was then decided that we would have to move into some pokey attic rooms at the top of the main building. We kicked up a fuss about this and because I had the biggest mouth I was identified as the ringleader and got the push.

Fortunately, I was able to get myself a job on a neighbouring farm in Hartpury, an outstanding feature of which was a magnificent 15th-century tithe barn, one of the largest and best preserved in the country, which served as a cow shed. The farm owner, Mr Powell, also had an interest in horses, mostly hunters, and I got to help him break them in. It turned out that I had a way with horses and I hadn't been there long before Mr Powell's brother, who not only ran his own large farm at Bodenham in Herefordshire but also operated as a National Hunt trainer, invited me to go and work for him, helping out with the steeple chasers.

My new boss was a successful trainer – his two best horses while I was with him were named Royal Birthday and Ludd Valley – and I quite enjoyed the work, but, at the same time, I knew it wasn't really what I wanted to do for the rest of my life. While I was still trying to make up my mind about my long-term future fate then intervened when I was called up for National Service. I had been exempt as long as I was working at the agricultural college, but once I left I became eligible and it wasn't long before they caught up with me.

I found myself summoned to Oswestry where I was conscripted into the Royal Artillery 2/4 Irish Battery. The plan was that after basic training you went either to Cyprus or Germany but I spotted a notice on the selection board about the King's Troop Royal Horse Artillery. And when I told them about my experience with horses I was duly posted to St John's Wood in London.

The King's Troop specialises in ceremonial duties such as Trooping the Colour, the firing of Royal Salutes in Hyde Park on both royal anniversaries and state occasions and the provision of a gun carriage and team of black horses for state and military funerals. The Troop also performs the duties of the Queen's Life Guard at Horse Guards for one month each year.

The King's Troop on parade at St John's Wood

A home visit during my brief National Service

That certainly sounded preferable to square bashing on some bleak German parade ground or being shot at by EOKA terrorists in Nicosia! However, despite being permanently based in London one routinely had to have a series of regulation vaccinations against various tropical diseases. The day after I'd had my jabs I proceeded to pass out during a ceremonial parade that had been laid on especially for the Press so that they could stock up with photos to go with any articles that were written about the Troop during the course of the next year or so.

I was on lance duty that day – not mounted on a horse but merely standing with a lance as a marker for the guns – and all of a sudden I just keeled over. I was immediately shipped off to Queen Alexandra's nursing home for tests and although they couldn't find anything wrong with me I was informed that I was to be discharged forthwith since they couldn't take the risk of a soldier collapsing during high profile ceremonial duties. And so it was that with one lucky bound I was free, having served only six months of the usual two years National Service. As an extra bonus I wasn't even put on the Reservist list.

I went back briefly to farming. My father, through a contact of his, managed to fix me up with a job in Slapton in South Devon, working for a farmer called George G. "Gee-Gee" Knight. However, although the location was lovely and the people I was working with were very nice to me, I wasn't really happy. By now I had decided that there was no real future for me in farming because unless you were a farmer's son or were very wealthy the capital outlay involved in acquiring land and buying the machinery to work it was prohibitive. So for somebody in my position the only way forward was to carry on as a lowly farm hand in the hope that you might one day be able to work your way up to become a farm manager. I felt it was time to get some decent employment and after looking around for something in a related field, I went to work as a traveling rep for a company owned a chain of chemist's shops with branches in Wootton-under-Edge, Chipping Sodbury and Thornbury that was trying to build up its sales of veterinary products to farmers in the area.

Meanwhile, my three hives of bees had been rather sadly neglected since I lost my job at the college. They had stayed at Hartpury for a time immediately after I left, with Harry keeping an eye on them for me. Thereafter they had moved around quite a bit – first to my parents' garden in Clifton while I was doing my brief stint of National Service, then down to Slapton with me and, when I went to work for the chemists and started living at home with my parents again, back to Clifton.

It wasn't too long before I changed my job yet again, repping first for agricultural merchants Puddy's of Wedmore and then for Alfie Nicholls of Chipping Sodbury, a large and very progressive agricultural supplies company. They gave me a patch in North Somerset where I would not only be offering the same sort of veterinary products that I had been selling for the chemists and for Puddy's but also animal feeds, fertilisers, sprays and all manner of other stuff.

It was at this point that I also met my wife-to-be, Mary. While I was still a student at Hartpury college my sister had come up to visit me one weekend during the course of which she met and then started going out with one of my fellow students, Eric, whom she subsequently went on to marry. The two of them had been invited up to Herefordshire for the day to visit the family of a chap who was going out with one of Eric's sisters. Like me, Eric at this time was working as a travelling rep for a company selling agricultural sprays, but he had used up most of the very meagre private

 54

Mary in uniform as a ward sister at Warwick Hospital and the two of us on our wedding day

mileage allowance on his company car and certainly didn't have enough left to take him to Herefordshire and back. As I also had use of a company car, but with a slightly more generous private mileage allowance, he wondered if I would be prepared to drive him and my sister there if he paid for the petrol. I was assured that I would be made very welcome by his prospective brother-in-law's large farming family, which included two more brothers and two sisters.

As I had nothing better to do I thought – why not? So off we went together. And among those waiting to greet us when we arrived was Mary, one of the two sisters, who happened to have come home for the weekend from London, where she was training as a nurse at the Westminster Hospital. She and I got on rather well and from then on I started going up to London to see her whenever I had the opportunity. That was in 1961 and we got married two years later in September 1963, just a few months after Mary finished her training to become a fully qualified nurse. The wedding and reception took place in Leominster, Mary's hometown, after which we spent our honeymoon touring in the Lake District and Scotland. For the first few months of our married life we then lived in a caravan while awaiting completion of a new house on a residential estate in Clevedon that we had bought off plan.

Over the next few years I continued to work for Alfie Nicholls while Mary nursed first at the local cottage hospital in Clevedon and then, following the birth of our two children – Diane in 1965 and Stephen in 1966 – at the Ham Green Fever Hospital in Bristol, which, very conveniently, had a nursery attached where the children of hospital staff could be looked after during the day.

I had meanwhile expanded my beekeeping activities to the point where I had about twenty hives. Some of them were still at my parents' place in Bristol and later moved with them when they retired to a cottage in Old Sodbury, where, happily, there was quite a large garden. Others were dotted around various farms in the Clevedon area. I also had one or two on land owned by an ex-Gurkha officer named Colonel Brown, a lovely man who had a lot of bees and who gave me hives and all sorts of other bits and pieces in return for me giving him a hand with his beekeeping.

All this was happening at a time when the farming scene was changing in a way that was disadvantageous to independent supply companies like Alfie Nicholls. Farmers were getting together to form co-operative groups that would buy in supplies in bulk for their members, thereby cutting out the middle man. In the North Somerset and South Gloucestershire area, in particular, the likes of Alfie Nicholls were taking a hammering. I could sense that there was not going to be much of a future in the farming industry for people like me and decided that I should get out of agriculture altogether. Having made this decision, I answered a newspaper advert for a job as a rep for non-branded Compton-Parkinson lighting products, with a sales patch extending over eighteen counties!

When Compton-Parkinson was then taken over by Hawker-Siddeley, my department was closed down. But instead of being made redundant I was offered a new position with the company, working as a rep in the Midlands, with a 'patch' centred on Coventry. Being a bit of country boy, this was a prospect that frightened the pants off me because I thought of the Midlands as being heavily industrial. However, as a married man with a young family I couldn't really afford to say no and so, with the company agreeing to pay all our moving expenses, Mary and I packed our bags and headed for Warwickshire, settling in the village of Harbury. And my hives came with me.

By this time beekeeping had become a bit more than just a hobby and soon, with a total of around seventy hives dotted around a number of farms in the area, I was producing quite a reasonable amount of honey for sale locally. I simply used to market it as Warwickshire honey until one of our clients then suggested that I ought to have some sort of brand name. It was at that point that I started looking around for something distinctive and came up with the idea of Fosse Way Honey, along with a logo featuring the windmill at Chesterton, near Harbury.

I had seen a very good line drawing of the windmill by a local artist named Joe Bamford and approached him to ask if I could use it. When I explained to him what I wanted it for he offered to help with the design and then produced a collection of different labels from all over the country to give me some ideas. We laid them all out and had a brain-storming session but kept I coming back to Fosse Way and the windmill, which I felt was quite specific but at the same time didn't limit us geographically. Joe then came up with a design that featured a big flourish on the F of Fosse Way and I had the gummed labels printed in Leamington Spa, trying out various different shapes until we found the one that worked best on the honey jars.

It was at around this time that a very tempting offer came my way. The Oxfordshire-based Chiltern Honey Farm was one of the oldest-established commercial honey producers in the country, founded by the legendary and pioneering British beekeeper R.O.B (Robert Orlando Beater) Manley back in the 1930s. In the early 1970s Manley's long-time foreman and specialist queen rearer, Harry Wickens, was contemplating retirement and they were looking around for someone to be groomed as his successor. I spotted the advert that they placed in the beekeeping press and applied, not really thinking that I had much chance of actually getting the job given my lack of experience. But it turned out that Harry Ashforth at Hartpury College had given me a glowing reference and, next thing I knew, Harry Wickens was on the phone asking me to go along for an interview.

A quiet, country gentleman, Harry had been the backbone of the Manley enterprise for many years, responsible for much of the general management as well as the breeding of all the replacement queens. We got on very well at the interview and he obviously decided that despite my lack of commercial beekeeping experience he could knock me into shape before he finally retired because he offered me the job on the spot. And when I hesitated, he upped the salary.

Full-time jobs in commercial beekeeping have always been few and far between and this one represented a particularly attractive opportunity. Apart from the association with Manley, seen by many as the father of commercial beekeeping in this country, Chiltern Honey Farm was still one of the UK's biggest producers at the time, with around a thousand colonies spread across Oxfordshire, Berkshire and down into Hampshire. And the improved terms I was offered were extremely generous by the standards of the day – a salary of £1,600-a-year, with rented accommodation provided for just £5.50-a-week in a very nice house in nearby Preston Crowmarsh that had been Manley's original home. On the face of it, this was the kind of offer that no aspiring beekeeper could possibly refuse. And yet, after a great deal of thought, I decided that I would have to turn it down.

It was not an easy decision, but for personal and family reasons I came to the conclusion that I should stay where I was. The main considerations were that our children, Diane and Stephen, who by this time were aged six and five respectively, had just settled into school in Harbury, while Mary had fixed herself up with a part-time nursing position in a local hospital that she could fit conveniently around the kids' daily routine. And I myself had what seemed like a secure job, having just been poached from Compton-Parkinson by rival firm REM. To uproot the family for the second time in less than a year would be too disruptive, I felt. So, rather reluctantly, I had to tell Harry Wickens: "Thanks – but no thanks."

I soon had good reason to think that I'd probably made a terrible mistake when, no more than a few months later, REM suddenly declared me redundant. It became clear that they had only really wanted me for the contacts I had built up with Compton-Parkinson and once they had milked those from me they didn't waste any time before kicking me out.

Indirectly, I did have the satisfaction of getting revenge on them for the cynical and rather shabby way in which I felt they had treated me. I had put a tow bar on the company car I had been given when I joined them and this was left on when I handed it back. The guy who did all their vehicle

Harry Wickens – made me the kind of offer I almost couldn't refuse

Family portrait with Mary, Stephen and Diane

repairs in a basement garage then decided in his wisdom to take it off using an acetylene torch with the result that the petrol tank blew up and the entire office block above burned down. Very fortunately, nobody was hurt. When I heard about it afterwards I have to admit that I did have to smile to myself.

Meanwhile, after a spell on the dole during which I spent a lot of time in my workshop making new hives from salvaged wood, I decided to have a go at setting up Fosse Way Honey as a viable commercial beekeeping enterprise, inspired partly by the fact that the Chiltern Honey Farm had been prepared to offer me a job. That was what gave me the confidence to think seriously about going out on my own. My feeling was that if somebody else thought I was worth employing as a beekeeper, then maybe I could make a go of doing it for myself.

I then had a stroke of luck that made this a real possibility when, making use of my earlier dairy farming experience, I managed to land a small part-time contract with the Milk Marketing Board that involved testing local herds for milk quality. It didn't pay that much, but the regular monthly cheque I received, combined with the extra money that Mary was able to make from her nursing job, meant that we had enough coming in to keep us afloat while I tried to get Fosse Way up and running.

In this respect the Milk Marketing Board job was a perfect fit. Mainly a matter of keeping records and taking samples of milk that then went away with the tankers to be analysed and checked in the laboratories, it meant visiting twelve or thirteen herds each month – and it wasn't long before many of the farmers whose herds I was checking had some of my hives on their land! A lot of them became good friends who, over the years, gave me introductions to friends and relatives of theirs who also took my hives. And they even employed me to do odd jobs that helped to tide me over during the winter months when there wasn't much happening with the bees – everything from putting up guttering to tiling bathrooms.

So, one way and another, it was that MMB contract that I have to thank for providing the springboard that launched my career as a full-time commercial beekeeper.

5: Queens of Australia

During the early days of Fosse Way Honey it was a bit of a struggle to make ends meet and there were moments when I again found myself regretting that I hadn't gone ahead and taken the job at Manley's Chiltern Honey Farm. However, as things eventually turned out it proved to have been a good decision, the company going out of business not that many years later.

By that time it had been reduced to operating as the relatively minor UK honey producing arm of Manley Ratcliffe, a larger company formed when Manley took over Ratcliffe Brothers of Bingley, packers of imported honey, with the aim of developing that particular side of the business. Following the deaths of both R.O.B Manley himself and his nephew John Manley, who had been helping him to run the business in the later years, the management was effectively overseen by accountants who decided that the UK production side was surplus to requirements and shut it down completely in order to concentrate on satisfying the rapidly growing demand from supermarkets for cheaper foreign imports. Oliver Field, who had taken the job I had been offered, took on the hives and bees and set up on his own as a bee farmer and beekeeping consultant, while Harry Wickens also went out on his own with the queen-rearing side. Later, company secretary Laurie Keys started up his own packing company, Honeysuckle Products, which he eventually sold to Chivers before going on to run Cotswold Speciality Foods.

While all this was going on I had been working overtime to turn what had been a hobby into a commercially viable business. In doing so, I was helped by the fact that when I finally decided to take the plunge I already had some seventy hives spread around the local area – too many for a hobby beekeeper but quite enough to form a good solid basis on which to start up a business.

My aim at the outset was to have a total of between 200-300 hives – although I did eventually end up with more than 350. In the first few years there was a need to expand fairly fast, something that can't always easily be done simply by creating new colonies from your existing stock, except at the expense of the short-term honey crop. The way I got round that particular problem was to import Caucasian queens from Australia each April, just as the Australian summer was coming to an end and our spring was beginning. I would take small divisions from those of my colonies that had wintered well and introduce the new queens. These fresh colonies would then have time to build up to full strength during the summer, towards the end of which they would be fit and ready to be moved up to the heather moors to produce a decent crop of top quality honey.

I chose to go with Caucasians, as against other varieties such as Italians or Carnolians, because they are good all-rounders. Italians have a reputation for being highly prolific, but you can have a job trying to stop them breeding when winter sets in and you're likely to lose them from starvation if you don't feed them all the time, while Carnolians are good bees but have a tendency to swarm. Caucasians, on the other hand, are reasonably productive, relatively easy to handle and not inclined to swarm too readily, making them ideal for achieving the sort of rapid increases in stock that I was looking for.

I got my queens from a top Australian queen breeder named Langridge, a great character who was always a delight to deal with. They cost me £5 each back in those days and were sent over in batches of twenty or thirty at a time in small cages about twice the size of a matchbox, each cage containing one queen and about six attendant workers to keep her clean and fed, with food provided in the form of a small, round piece of candy like the baker's fondant you find on the top of sticky buns. They would come by regular airmail and would usually arrive three days after being despatched from Down Under, delivered along with the rest of the post. Bees are actually the only livestock that the UK postal system is allowed to deliver – an interesting little fact that might make a good pub quiz question. However, when the consignments arrived in the sorting room at our local Harbury post office, which was part of the village shop where my honey happened to be on sale, I would often get a phone call from sub-postmaster and store owner Brian Taylor announcing that my 'livestock' had come in and politely suggesting that I might like to go and pick it up myself. He knew full well that the post lady we had in those days would be a little apprehensive about going out with a parcel that buzzed alarmingly in the carrier of her delivery bike!

URGENT. LIVE QUEEN BEES

MR. JOHN HOME.
23, FRANCES ROAD,
HARBURY,
LEAMINGTON SPA.
WARWS.   CV33·9JG.

Queens came from Australia by post

Within three years I had managed to increase the total number of my hives from around seventy to more than two hundred-and-fifty. A lot of these I built myself out of bits of salvaged wood that I picked up here and there, including pallets, on some of which you would be lucky enough to find very useful sheets of plywood. That kept me busy in my workshop during every spare moment.

In addition, I was fortunate to be able to buy a large number of hives from another commercial beekeeper, Jim Dawes, who was gradually scaling down the business started by his father, Charlie, who also happened to be the local distribution agent for El Dorado ice cream. When beekeeping hit a bad patch, Charlie concentrated on the ice cream business while Jim, who was a talented self-taught joiner and cabinet maker, went round the local antique shops to see whether they had anything that might need renovating. One of them gave him a large Welsh dresser that they wanted cut down in size and he made such a good job of it that the work soon started pouring in, with the result that the beekeeping became more and more of a sideline. It was then that Jim contacted me to ask if I would be interested in taking over a few of his hives, which I was more than happy to do, especially as I also got the farm sites where they were located.

Over the next two or three years I eventually took over all but about ten of his hives. Altogether I had over one hundred from him and because I was

63

At work on hives in the
Warwickshire countryside

tight for cash we agreed an arrangement whereby I paid him in honey that he continued to sell to his regular customers. Then, when I had paid off the full amount, he took me round all the shops that he supplied and introduced me, saying: "It's actually John's honey you've been buying for the last couple of years!" So, of course, I was then able to take over all the accounts. For me it was a very good all-round deal. It put up my hive numbers substantially, provided me with a lot of new sites and also, at a stroke, presented me with a whole lot of new outlets in places in the Cotswolds where I had not previously been established.

With all my extra hives I was by now producing a crop of up to eight tonnes of honey a season. I had decided at the outset that instead of simply producing as much honey as I possibly could and selling it on in bulk to one of the big honey packers, which is how many commercial beekeepers operate, I would rather have my own brand and sell it directly to local shops and any other outlets I could find. This was partly a matter of pride in being able to have my own brand up there on the shelves and partly because there were considerable financial and business advantages to be had from marketing it myself. One of the problems with selling to the packers was that if you had a bad season there might not be enough honey for them to bother with, in which case they didn't want to buy it from you. On the other hand, if there was a lot of honey about they would want to pay less for it, so you were liable to get caught either way. On top of which, they only paid out once or twice a year which could cause cash flow problems. By marketing it myself I could not only get better price but was also assured of steady sales and a regular cash flow.

On the debit side, doing things this way involved a lot of extra work. As a one-man band I was not only beekeeping manager but also marketing and distribution manager, packing manager, transport manager and stock controller – a real Jack-of-all-trades. And although I did feel right from the start that I understood all that was needed on the livestock management side, I was aware that I still had a lot to learn when it came to essential office and business skills. Among other things, I had to make sure I knew how to keep proper records and accounts, including everything relating to tax and VAT, while also staying on top of the latest trading standards regulations and various environmental health issues and dealing with a whole lot of other tiresome and time-consuming paperwork.

My first priority early on was obviously to establish a lot more outlets through which to sell my honey and the only way to do this was to follow former Conservative minister Norman Tebbit's famously controversial advice to the jobless to "get on your bike" – or, in my case, a rather clapped out, half-timbered Morris Traveller – and go out knocking on shop doors with a load of samples in search of new business.

The slight problem in this respect was that the Traveller was the only vehicle I could afford to run at the time and I had to share it with Mary, who regularly needed it to get to and from her part-time nursing jobs, often at times when I also needed it for work. This situation was clearly unsatisfactory but at that stage I simply didn't have the money with which to buy the sort of van I really should have had right from the start. The solution came when I heard about a Swedish gentleman who was going around the country buying up supplies of propolis, the sticky resin that bees use to seal gaps in their hives. Propolis is one of nature's marvels, containing various antibiotic, anti-viral and anti-inflammatory properties that can be extracted and used in certain dental and medical products and this Swedish buyer was offering beekeepers no less than £5-an-ounce for supplies that he then sold on to the pharmaceutical industry back in Scandinavia.

Keen to take full advantage of this welcome opportunity to earn some much-needed extra cash I spent hours in the middle of what was a very bitter winter sitting in the freezing cold barn in Barford where I kept a lot of my equipment stored at the time, scraping every bit of propolis off my hives by the light of a Tilley lamp. It was well worth all the effort, however, because I ended up with about £300-worth of the stuff and used the money to invest in an old blue Bedford van, which I bought from a man who ran a market traders' warehouse next to the Peugeot engine plant in the centre of Coventry.

I was very pleased with the van, but couldn't understand why it was that whenever I was driving it around in the Coventry area other drivers would flash their lights and wave at me. At first I thought they must be trying to warn me that something was wrong with the van or that there was a police speed trap ahead, but this never actually seemed to be the case and after a while I would just grin and wave back, thinking: 'That's strange – I never realised so many people in Coventry knew me.' This remained something of a mystery until all was explained some months later when I picked up the local Coventry Evening Telegraph one day to read that the market traders' warehouse had burned down in circumstances that led to the man from whom I had bought the van appearing in court along with his wife, who, it emerged, had been running a brothel above the shop premises across the road! It was there that I had actually gone to hand over the money for the van, which had obviously remained familiar to quite a few of madam's satisfied clients!

With the transport problem sorted out I was able to redouble my efforts to go out on the road in search of new customers in the surrounding towns and villages of South Warwickshire, North Oxfordshire, Worcestershire and Northamptonshire, doing the rounds of town centre shops, village stores, farm shops, garden centres and so on. At the same time, it became possible for me to move a few hives up to the Derbyshire heather moors at the end of each season, adding prized heather honey to Fosse Way's range of products. I was also in a position to start taking on pollination contracts that, over the years, were regularly to take me as far afield as the orchards of Kent as well as to the nearby market gardens of the Vale of Evesham.

Pollination contracts are an important element of any commercial beekeeper's business, not only providing a substantial, guaranteed income but also helping to ensure a good and varied honey crop. When I first started up in business the going rate was £20-per-hive-per-month, a figure that has since risen to around £50. And at my peak I would regularly have 120 hives out at the height of the season throughout April, May and June.

Everything is organised through the Bee Farmers Association's National Pollination Scheme, which matches individual beekeepers with particular farmers and growers, depending on availability, location, the number of hives required and other relevant factors. The Association then collects the money on the beekeeper's behalf, guaranteeing payment even if the grower goes belly up.

You often have to wait quite a while after signing up before you get your first contract. I wasn't offered anything in the first year but then, in the second year, the secretary, Mr Secker, rang to say that there was a small contract available at a mixed orchard in Kent owned by a Mr Bryce. He only needed twenty or thirty hives so it didn't really make much sense commercially for me to go all that way, but I reckoned it was well worth it just to get a foot in the door of the Pollination Scheme.

Normally, once you had established contact, you would tend to return to the same orchard every year, but Mr Bryce closed down shortly afterwards – as many other British growers have sadly had to do since then. I moved on to Payne's, a very large fruit farm just outside Sittingbourne that included 500 acres of Bramley apple trees, plus Worcesters and a considerable acreage of pears. I stayed with them for many years. The association began in 1985 when there was a devastating loss of bees throughout this country and the demand for pollination was desperate. I was contacted to see if I could help out and took a load of hives down for the pears. The farm manager then asked if he could move them on to the apples, along with any others I could let him have. From that time on we built up a relationship that soon involved taking down two loads of sixty hives every season before Payne's, too, eventually succumbed to the steadily falling demand for traditional English apple varieties in recent years that has resulted in so many of Kent's once flourishing orchards being laid waste, with a consequent drop in the demand for pollination contracts. For that we have to blame the supermarkets, who find it cheaper and more convenient to import foreign varieties such as

Hives amid Bramley apple trees in a Kentish orchard

With Clive Joyce, giving a demonstration at the Royal Show. We were criticized for not wearing full protective gear

Golden Delicious, Granny Smith, Braeburn and Gala. Nobody seems to buy home-grown cooking apples such as Bramleys any more and even most of the Cox's come from abroad.

I have rather fond memories of those forays down to Kent – driving through the heart of London in the wee small hours, in the days before the M25, in order to get to the apple orchards in time to get the hives set up before sunrise, when the bees start to forage. Not surprisingly, I would regularly be pulled over by suspicious police patrol cars wanting to check exactly what business I had driving a van around at that time of the night.

I would usually be accompanied on these trips by one or other of several experienced beekeeping friends who were more than happy to help me out by lending a hand every now and again, whenever required – people like John Creedy from Coventry, Jack Hood and Barry Baxter from Nuneaton and Clive Joyce from Kenilworth.

Clive Joyce is well known in beekeeping circles, having looked after the British Beekeepers Association's apiary at the Royal Agricultural Society Showground at Stoneleigh for more than thirty years, while also serving as the Royal Society's Honey Steward. His passion for beekeeping had begun in his mid-thirties after he had watched a demonstration at the Royal Show. A dedicated hobby beekeeper who never aspired to be a commercial bee farmer, he has always kept a colony at his home in Kenilworth, supplying friends and neighbours with honey and spending a great deal of his time encouraging others to take up beekeeping. Hugely supportive right from the earliest days of Fosse Way Honey, he was always ready to come over for a day's beekeeping.

John Creedy was secretary of the Coventry Beekeepers Association for many years at a time when, because there wasn't quite the same interest in hobby beekeeping that there is today, he had his work cut out just to keep the club going. An accountant by profession, John was a very good beekeeper – meticulous about the way things should be done and, consequently, none too impressed by my willingness to cut the odd corner here and there! Already in his late seventies and long retired by the time I got to know him, he was still so enthusiastic that he was quite prepared to get up well before dawn and walk two or three miles from his home in Coventry to a spot on the ring road where I would pick him up at 5.00am on the way to the heather moors. I would find him sitting there on the verge with his tucker bag, ready to jump into the van and drive up to Derbyshire with me. Once the hives had been set up we would sit for a while with a cup of coffee as the sun came up and on one particularly glorious morning I remember him remarking with a shake of his head: "They can go on their continental holidays, but how can you beat a view like this?" As we finished our coffee he would invariably reach into his tucker bag, bring out a hip flask and say with a conspiratorial grin: "You'll have a drop, won't you?" It was a pleasure for him to help me out and he particularly loved those trips to the moors – although he wouldn't always stay awake on the journey home!

John used to have to get up even earlier when he accompanied me down to Kent – driving himself over to my place in Harbury in time for a 3.00am getaway. He used to say that wherever he went with me we always seemed to have some excitement along the way – and this usually involved being stopped by suspicious policemen. The first time it happened was shortly after I'd replaced the Bedford van with an LDV. We'd hardly pulled out of the yard at Harbury when a patrol car passed us going in the opposite direction. A few minutes later it suddenly re-appeared right behind us and after following us for a while overtook us with lights flashing and pulled us over. I shouted to John to put his seat belt on and climbed out of the van.

"Good morning, Sir. Would you mind telling me what you've got on board?" inquired the officer, a question with which I was to become quite familiar over the next few years.

"Honey bees, going to Kent for orchard work," I replied.

"I see. Well, are you aware that you've got different registration plates on the van and the trailer?"

I had only just bought the van and realised with an awful sinking feeling that I had completely forgotten to change the registration plate on the trailer. I was actually quite impressed that the policemen had taken a note of the number going both ways. Having checked that I was the owner of both registrations they let me off with a caution, wishing me a safe journey. I told them very sincerely that it was comforting to know that there were chaps like them driving around in the middle of the night keeping an eye on things and they warned me that vans – especially vans with trailers – were always regarded as suspicious when they were spotted out and about in the early hours.

On another occasion we were pulled over late on a summer's night on our way back from Derbyshire, having loaded up the hives as dusk fell over the moors. After asking the routine questions about where we were going and what we'd got on board the officer walked round the back of the van to check and shone his powerful torch onto the hives in the trailer. Of course, if you shine a strong beam on hives that have had the roof taken off and replaced with a travelling screen the bees will come straight up to the light, making a bit of a roar! The policeman jumped back in shock, yelling to his mate: "Better get back in the car!" It turned out that the reason he'd stopped me was that the offside light on the trailer wasn't working, but he couldn't

Jack Hood helping me to unload hives on the moors

wait to get on his way and again let me off with a warning.

Compared to John Creedy, Jack Hood's methods were a bit rough and ready and yet he too was an excellent, semi-commercial beekeeper. He worked as a railwayman but kept a large number of hives and, like John, sold his honey to the packers. Now sadly no longer with us, he was a great character, a down-to-earth countryman who always kept a Springer spaniel and who loved shooting, ferreting and beating for shoots. He was one of the first people to encourage and help me with my beekeeping and it was through him that I was able to bag prime sites for my hives on the ling heather moors of the Chatsworth estate in Derbyshire. Jack had been going up there for years to work as a beater for the shoots and he started taking me with him, introducing me to all his contacts among the gamekeepers and their staff.

As beaters, we would be paid £5-a-day, plus a bottle of beer at lunchtime. Jack always wore leggings over his trousers and a voluminous jacket with big inside pockets into which he would stuff any rabbits that his dog happened to pick up. This was against the rules but the gamekeepers, who knew full well what was going on, would turn a blind eye, simply calling out pointedly: "Hey, Jack, you ain't half putting on weight!"

Having got to know head gamekeeper Dick Norris and his staff, I managed to get permission to put hives on the three sites on the moors that I have been using ever since. Once Fosse Way Honey was up and running my annual routine would involve going to the Kent orchards in May, followed by the Vale of Evesham bean fields in late May and early June and then up to the moors in August, which is when the heather comes into bloom. The general rule used to be that you would go up to the moors on or around August 12th – 'The Glorious 12th' when shooting begins – but the seasons seem to have altered in recent years, the heather is flowering earlier and now you really need to be up there by the end of July or the beginning of August at the latest.

Big, strong and powerfully built, Barry Baxter, another good friend and regular helper over the years, was always a particularly useful man to have with you when it came to moving hives around the country to the orchards and the moors. He could quite easily lift a hive on and off the trailer on his own, without any help from me. In fact, when we were working together I

71

used to think that he could probably have hoisted me onto the trailer along with the hive!

I would generally reckon to leave the bees up on the moors for about a month, although there is no hard and fast rule in this respect. As always, much depends on the weather. If the peat gets too dry the plants will economise and produce less nectar, leading to a reduced honey crop. Ideally, you need plenty of rain in May, the optimum time as far as heather is concerned. Being a woody plant, it doesn't respond immediately to moisture, but a suitably wet spring encourages growth and ensures good summer blossom and maximum nectar, enabling the bees to produce a bumper crop.

Hives set up on the heather moors

I recall one such season when Mary and I and the kids happened to be going off on a family holiday in the Peak District of Derbyshire and I used the opportunity to hitch the trailer to the back of the car and take some of the hives up to the moors a bit earlier than usual. After the holiday I went back up with the rest of the hives and found, much to my surprise, that the advance party had produced a huge crop in just ten days.

Those who consider themselves to be connoisseurs of honey tend to insist that heather honey is the best and it certainly has a very distinctive, quite pungent flavour. Fosse Way produces both a pure heather honey and what we call an 'English' honey, a blend that is part heather and part local and therefore not quite as strong-tasting as the pure heather honey. The problem with producing single source specialist honeys is that you can end up making a rod for your own back insofar as it can be difficult to maintain the consistency of colour, texture and taste that regular customers expect. For that reason I have mostly steered away from them in favour of a mix of light and dark honeys, predominantly from the fields and hedgerows of Warwickshire, but with some input from the Kentish apple orchards and the market gardens of the Vale of Evesham as well as from the Derbyshire heather moors.

As it happens, our regular best seller has always been a soft set creamed honey that is easier to spread than the regular hard, crystallised, set honeys. This is produced by a two-stage process that firstly involves selecting a fine-textured honey, drawing it off into containers, putting it in store and allowing it to set in the normal way before then gently warming it until it reaches the consistency of porridge. After bottling, it is left to set again, but remains soft enough to spread, never setting quite as hard the second time around.

I think that probably the best honey we ever produced came out of one of the orchards in Kent, where the bees had feasted on nectar from a mix of apple blossom, hawthorn, dandelion and other wild flowers that had been left to grow in profusion under the orchard trees. Normally, this would have been just one of the honeys that went into the mix but because it was so special I kept it to one side. This was back in the early days of Fosse Way when I was still doing a lot of showing and when I entered it in the National Honey Show in London it proved to be a winner.

I eventually stopped showing because it became too time-consuming. Apart from that, I've always felt that there is something slightly artificial about all such shows, whether it be Crufts, the Royal Show or even local county flower and vegetable shows. Dogs and cattle all tarted up, giant marrows and leeks, outsize blooms – very often it can seem a bit over the top. And when it comes to honey, the same prize sample can be entered over and over again. In fact, one beekeeper I know had a beautiful comb of honey which he kept showing and winning with year after year.

I did briefly come out of retirement in 2008 – mainly to support the honey section at what turned out to be the last-but-one Royal Show, but also to prove that I still knew how to show. And much to the frustration of the regulars, I swept the board, winning four 1st prizes for dark honey, ling heather honey, cut comb honey and dry mead, along with a 2nd prize for

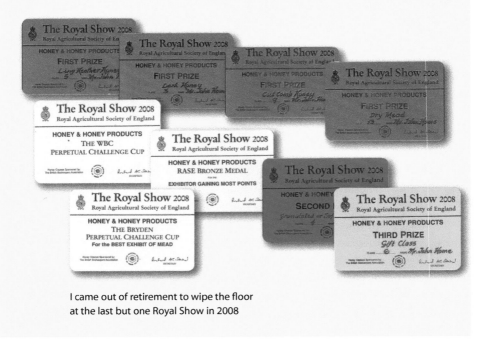

I came out of retirement to wipe the floor
at the last but one Royal Show in 2008

my soft set honey and a 3rd prize in the gift class, plus three special awards – one for the best exhibit of mead, one for the exhibitor gaining most points overall and, to top it all, the Best In Show award for my dark honey.

As it happens, that big winner of mine was basically a ten-year-old honey from a very special crop that I had kept aside because it was so exceptional. I couldn't be sure, but I suspected that it might have come from aphids that had been feeding on lime trees where the bees had been foraging. What happens is that the aphids suck the sap from the leaves of a tree and the bees then come along and suck it from the aphids. Some people might be put off by the thought of honey produced in this way and yet prized Black Forest honey from Germany comes mainly via aphids that have been feeding on pine trees. This dark honey of mine had a beautiful nutty flavour and a wonderful colour. To produce my award winning entry I warmed it into bottles, added some newer honey, filtered it again and re-bottled it. And although I say it myself, it did look and taste exceptional.

6: Busy Bee

By the late seventies Fosse Way Honey was fully established, with around 350 hives in more than thirty different locations spread all over Warwickshire, in an area that stretched from Princethorpe, just south of Coventry, in the north of the county to Tysoe in the south and from Loxley in the west across to Priors Hardwick in the east – about 300 square miles in all. With some of the shops and other outlets that I supplied even more widely dispersed and with annual trips taking bees to the Derbyshire heather moors, and to the Vale of Evesham and the Kentish orchards to fulfil pollination contracts, I routinely clocked up an annual mileage in excess of 50,000 miles.

Altogether, I was reckoning to harvest between ten and twelve tonnes of honey a season. And with a growing range of products that included several different types of set and runny honeys, some of them packaged in special pottery containers in the shape of everything from teddy bears and miniature bee hives to owls, hedgehogs, squirrels, rabbits and even frogs, plus other hive products that ranged from candles to beeswax furniture polish, annual turnover rose steadily to a peak of over £110,000.

By 1982 the business had already expanded to the point where it had outgrown the family home in Harbury and it was then that we moved to

The growing range of Fosse Way products

Deppers Bridge, where we have been ever since. The move turned out to be rather more hurried than expected because the house at Harbury sold almost as soon as we put it on the market and before we had had a chance to find a new place, catching us slightly on the hop. With nowhere to go to I was just starting to get a bit anxious when, on my way to check some hives that I had sited on land near the old cement works at Deppers Bridge, I noticed a 'For Sale' sign being out up outside what seemed like an ideal property. Just a mile down the road from the Harbury house, it came with a double garage and a sizeable shed in which to carry on the business as well as a good-sized piece of land on which to put some hives. Instead of carrying on to visit the hives at the cement works I turned round, went straight back home and got Mary to ring the agent, whose number was on the board, to arrange a viewing. Having had a good look round we then made an offer on the spot and within a matter of days the deal was done and we were able to start moving in.

Although I was still basically running the whole Fosse Way operation single-handedly, it would not have been strictly true to describe myself as a one-man-band. I employed two local housewives who came in to work for a few hours each week – cutting the combs, extracting, bottling, labeling and packing the honey during the season and then, in winter, helping to assemble the woodwork for new hives or existing ones that were in need of renovation. And at the height of the season I would sometimes take on a foreign student or someone else from the local college as a part-time casual labourer during the summer vacation.

Sylvan Borneck at work in the Canaries, grafting eggs for queen cells

This still left more than enough work to keep me busy from dawn until dusk for all but a couple of weeks in January when Mary and I would escape briefly for a winter break in the Canaries. Even that usually turned out to be a bit of a busman's holiday because while there I would always make a point of looking up a great beekeeping friend of mine named Sylvan Borneck and would inevitably end up giving him a hand now and again during our stay. I actually found it quite therapeutic and Sylvan and his wife were always extremely hospitable to both Mary and me so it was an enjoyable experience.

Back at home my routine, weather permitting, was based around regular weekly visits to each of the thirty-odd hive sites to carry out general management checks and to take off any boxes in which the combs were 'ripe' with honey. The nectar sources at each of the sites would vary according to the location and the time of year, but in many cases the predominant source for the early honey crop from farmland sites would be oilseed rape. The only problem with that is that honey produced from oilseed rape sets very hard in the comb, meaning that it can't easily be spun out in a centrifuge in the usual way.

In the 1970s, when oilseed rape suddenly became the break crop of choice for most arable farmers and the countryside started disappearing under a blanket of yellow every spring, the only answer seemed to be to take the honey boxes off as soon as they were ready, spinning the honey out of the combs overnight before it had a chance to set and then returning the drawn combs to the hives the following morning in readiness for the next nectar flow. However, the need to repeat this process two or three times while the

In spring oilseed rape turns the countryside yellow

77

bees were working the rape obviously involved a huge amount of extra work as I would end up having to bring back and deal with anything up to nine hundred boxes over a fairly short period of time.

To get round this I and one or two other commercial bee farmers developed a modified system of hive management. For the uninitiated, a hive will usually have a stack of three or four standard honey boxes known as 'supers', each containing a number of natural, ready-made combs. Because the bees have built them on a wire-reinforced wax sheet provided by the beekeeper as a foundation to make their job easier, these combs are robust enough to be spun without breaking up and can then be returned empty to the hive to be refilled with honey. Instead of this arrangement, the modified system involves having just one 'super' and, above that, two or three self-build 'cutter' boxes, added as and when needed. The frames suspended within these 'cutter' boxes are fitted not with wired foundation sheets but with small pieces of starter strip on which the bees build combs that, when filled with honey, can be cut from the frame as a whole.

The combs are then gently warmed in a thermostatically-controlled melting cabinet that gradually liquidises the hard set honey and the wax together, the wax separating and floating to the surface, leaving the pure honey to be drawn off. This means that after spinning the honey out of the first 'super' as soon as it is ready you can happily leave what is in the 'cutters' to set. This can then be taken off at any time and stored until the relatively quiet winter months when you can process it at your leisure.

There are those who tend to be a bit sniffy about this warming process – which was originally designed simply to treat that part of any comb that has to be sliced away before the honey can be spun off in the centrifuge. There is a suggestion that it is akin to pasteurization and that it somehow compromises the natural goodness and full nutritional value of the honey. I have never accepted this, stressing that it is a matter of very gentle warming rather than heating. And an added advantage is that the wax produced in this way is of the highest quality.

Those who turn their noses up at the idea of the warming process also tend to be very uncomplimentary about the quality of oilseed rape honey generally. "Lard-like" is one highly derogatory description used by some people, mostly urban beekeepers keen to promote the idea that their early season honey is superior to that produced in the countryside precisely because their town bees are able to enjoy a much more varied diet at a time of year when their country cousins are forced to feed almost exclusively on oilseed rape. Such exaggerated criticism is unjustified in my view and in my more mischievous moments I might be tempted to hit back with equally unfair comments about the possible effects of exhaust-fumed inner city pollution and whether one would really want to eat honey produced from cut flowers left on cemetery graves!

However, I would have to agree that oilseed rape does not perhaps yield the best quality honey. It is very pale in colour and the taste is indeed rather bland. And yet at the same time it does, like other brassica honeys, have one excellent characteristic in that although it sets hard it actually has a very fine, smooth texture. So, once I'd got the extraction process sorted out I was more than happy to use it because it would only ever be one type of honey in the very varied mix that went into Fosse Way's standard, award-winning Warwickshire honeys.

Fosse Way's standard award-winning honeys –
soft set and runny honey from the Warwickshire
countryside and English honey, a soft set mix of
Warwickshire and heather honey

The thirty different well-spaced sites on which my hives were located ensured a wide range of nectar sources through the season – from the sweet chestnuts of Oakley Wood, which produced an especially beautiful honey crop, to the clover on the school sports fields near the Myton Road site between Warwick and Leamington that also gave the bees access to the limes and sycamores growing in both the towns' public parks. A farm at Wasperton Hill sometimes grew sunflowers that as well as giving very distinctive honey also produced wonderful yellowy, pinkish wax; another at North End grew beans. At various times throughout the season there would also be tree and hedgerow blossom – mostly hawthorn, blackthorn, horse chestnut, lime and blackberry – along with every kind of wildflower, not to mention the cultivated flowers, shrubs and vegetables of country house gardens and allotments. So, one way and another, my country bees benefited from a diet as varied and well-balanced as anything available in town, if not more so.

In marketing terms, consistency of taste, texture, quality and constant availability is all-important for a commercial beekeeper. The clients you supply need to know exactly what they're getting and also that there will be a steady unbroken supply, which is why, when it came to my brand leaders, I went for a mixture (I don't like the word blend). The Warwickshire honeys, both runny and soft-set, were great all-rounders that I knew I could repeat year after year, regardless of variations in the weather and any other local environmental factors. And in order to guarantee that I could keep the shops and my other regular clients fully stocked, even in a bad year, I made sure that I always had at least half-a-year's supply held in reserve.

As well as the standard Warwickshire honeys, Fosse Way also produced several types of specialist honey in limited quantities. They included a light borage honey, a heavy, dark, pungent heather honey, an English honey, a Cotswold honey and even a honey with added apricots, not to mention honey mustard! These more specialist products were sold mostly from our stands at the big shows – the Royal Show at Stoneleigh and the BBC Good Food Show at the NEC in Birmingham – but also at the local farmers' markets where we would regularly have a stall. With one exception, everything we sold, including the beeswax candles and furniture polish, was produced at Deppers Bridge by myself and my two part-time helpers. The exception was our honey fudge, which was made by a company in Scotland using honey that we sent up in large containers.

Our stand at the BBC Good Food Show

Grandchildren (l to r) Andrew, Becky and Katherine helping me out on our stall at the Town & Country Festival, held at the Royal Showground at Stoneleigh

Looking back, I do sometimes wonder how I managed to fit it all in – especially during the six years in the 1980s when, on top of everything else, I also became fully involved with the UK Bee Farmers Association at a critical time for the beekeeping industry.

During the season, from spring until autumn, my regular working day would start in the yard at Deppers Bridge where I would spend the first couple of hours preparing for the day ahead. Among other duties, I would get the next batch of honey ready to be packed, checking the quality and deciding what we needed to have in stock – so many half-pound jars, so many 1lb jars, so many teddy bear gift pots and so on.

The various different gift pots had started out as a novelty but soon became an important part of the business. The teddy bears, skeps and straightforward honeypots sold especially well in shops that catered for tourists in places such as Stratford on Avon and around the Cotswolds. And at Christmas our Father Christmases and snowmen were much in demand. Apart from their direct sales value the giftware also helped to boost sales generally because every time a shop ran out of bunnies or teddy bears or any one of the novelty items, the manager would often tend to make up a full order, topping up his stock of all the other products as well. The wider your range, the better this would work, so although each new gift pot design and initial mould would cost between £500 and £800 to produce it was still very worthwhile in the long run.

Once I had got everything in order at Deppers Bridge I would load up the van for maybe a couple of deliveries to customers, probably dropping in at a couple of farm sites on the way back. Then, depending on the weather, I would be out again visiting other sites to carry out routine management – maybe introducing new queens to a colony, trying to stop bees from swarming, making sure there were enough boxes on each hive and bringing back any boxes that were full of ripe combs. By the end of the day I might have a vanload of honey boxes to be unloaded and put in a warm room overnight ready for extraction the next day.

This routine would be interrupted in late spring and early summer by pollination trips, firstly to Kent for the fruit orchards and then to the Vale of Evesham for the runner beans. In late summer the stronger colonies would be moved up to the Derbyshire heather moors. The reason I would take only the stronger colonies is that the bees have to work harder at that time of year because the days are getting shorter and so they need to be in good shape. In particular, those that had been working the borage immediately before the time came to move up to Derbyshire would probably be clapped out. This is because the borage is very hard on the bees, which have to force their heads into the heart of the flower in order to get at the nectar. Their wings become frayed as a result and the very fine down on their bodies gets worn out. So I would never take bees that have been working borage to the moors.

The average person probably never thinks of bees as livestock in the same way as cattle or sheep, but to a beekeeper that is exactly what they are. And like any good stockman, an experienced beekeeper will not only know how to manage them, handle them and look after their well-being but will also become sensitive to their moods and behaviour patterns. For instance, it is noticeable that bees' moods are influenced by the nectar sources that they are working at any given time. In particular, they can sometimes get irritable and aggressive when feeding on brassicas such as oilseed rape. And

Hives in a field of borage in Warwickshire. Bees have to work harder than usual when foraging on borage

when they all start streaming back to the hive in the middle of the day for no apparent reason you can be sure the weather is about to change for the worse. Once again, you have to be on your guard if that happens because at a time like that they don't want you working in the hive.

It is that sort of awareness that enables experienced beekeepers like me to work around the bees a lot of the time without much in the way of protective clothing. I'm always being asked how often I get stung and the answer is that I very rarely get stung at all. And on those rare occasions when it does happen I hardly experience any reaction. I guess you just become immune after a time. I got to know a local council pest control officer who would always call me in to help if he had to deal with what turned out to be a wild honeybee nest or swarm and he was amazed to see me pop a large swarm into a cardboard box with my bare hands. But there's actually very little risk if you know what you're doing. Mind you, I wouldn't ever try it with those belligerent Kenyan bees!

There was a time when I used to get called out quite often to deal with swarms, although that doesn't happen so much now that wild honeybees have mostly disappeared. For many years, bees always used to nest in a cavity in the stonework of the church at Chesterton, just above the main door. They would swarm quite regularly, often attaching themselves to a tombstone close to the path through the churchyard. For some reason, this always seemed to happen just before a wedding was due to take place, at which point I would get an emergency call from the church warden. Another regular nest site on my patch was a hollow tree near the war memorial in Ufton and there always used to be nests in the stonework at both Stoneleigh Abbey and Ragley Hall. Nowadays, however, wild nests are few and far between, largely as a result of the parasitic Varroa mite.

By the time the bees come back from the heather moors in September the season is coming to an end. But there is always a surge in demand for honey from the shops in the autumn and also in the last few weeks leading up to Christmas, which is when the gift ware, especially, starts disappearing off the shelves. So we would be busier than ever extracting, packing and delivering. But at the beginning of the New Year shopkeepers traditionally don't want to buy anything – they're too busy either licking their wounds or counting their takings! So that is when Mary and I would take the opportunity to go off to the Canaries for our annual winter break, during which we would always spend time with Sylvan Borneck, his wife and daughter.

As soon as we got back I would be in the workshops, cleaning and repairing up to fifty hives each year with new timber, each piece of which has to be put through a pan of boiling paraffin wax in order to make it waterproof. At the same time I would be preparing to introduce new queens in early spring in order to start fresh colonies to replace those that had not managed to survive the winter. And then, almost before you knew it, the new season would be upon you.

Me hard at work in the bottling plant at Deppers Bridge

84

When you are running a business on your own, especially one like beekeeping that involves a fair amount of hard physical outdoor work, staying fit and healthy becomes vitally important. This was brought home to me very early on when I was grounded out of the blue by an unexpected health problem.

It had been a long and very busy day. I had first driven my mother back to Bristol from Harbury, where she had been staying with us for the weekend. Having dropped her off, I then continued straight on from Bristol across to Kent to pick up a load of hives from one of the orchards where I had a pollinating contract. After waiting for the bees to return to the hives at dusk I started the lengthy job of single-handedly loading them onto the pick-up truck and eventually set out for home late in the evening. Driving through the early hours I became aware that my vision in one eye was strangely impaired, as if I was looking through the frosted glass in a bathroom window. It was no better when I woke up the next morning so I took myself off to the doctor. He diagnosed a detached retina and booked me into hospital on the spot. He wanted me to be admitted straightaway but I explained that I had a bit of beekeeping to do first and it was agreed that as long as I took it easy and promised not to eat anything in the meantime I could report to the hospital at 6.00 am the next morning.

I was in hospital for five days altogether. There was no laser treatment in those days – it was a straightforward welding job! And when I was discharged I was horrified to be told that I mustn't do any lifting or bending for three months. Well, there's no way you can do beekeeping in the middle of the season without lifting and bending so I would have been in serious trouble if it hadn't been for good friends like John Creedy and Jack Hood coming to my rescue. They did most of the lifting for me and, whenever necessary, I got round the bending simply by kneeling on plastic fertilizer sacks.

The next crisis arose when my hip started giving out. I soldiered on as long as possible but it got to the point where the pain was so crippling that the only way I could walk was by 'throwing' the affected hip out stiffly, my gait gradually becoming more and more ungainly. I was told at first that because, at the time, I was still only in my very early fifties I was considered too young for a hip replacement. However, I persisted and they eventually agreed to carry out the operation in December 1992, with the severe warning that I needed to change my job and my work lifestyle in order to protect the new hip which, I was told, would anyway only last eight years at the outside. Of course, changing my job was never really an option as far as I was concerned – and twenty years later that hip is still fine.

Fortunately, because the operation was done in the middle of winter, my being out of action for a few weeks afterwards while I convalesced hardly caused any disruption to the business. At that time of year it's mainly a matter of delivering supplies to the shops in the run-up to Christmas and I managed to get that done before I went in. And January is always quiet.

Seven years later when I had the other hip replaced I decided to have it done privately, mainly because the NHS couldn't guarantee to do the operation during the winter. By going private I was able to arrange a convenient date in February 1999, a time of year when things are still pretty quiet on the beekeeping front. And with Mary taking over driving duties while I acted purely as navigator we were able to carry on pretty much as usual.

On the day of the operation my surgeon came to check me out and said as he left: "I'm now going to get the anaesthetist to come in and see you," adding with a smile: "His name is Dr White. I think you two will get on very well."

Rather to my surprise, Dr White then turned out to be a delightful West Indian gentleman who was keen to talk to me about beekeeping, having done a bit of it himself on his parents' farm back home in the Caribbean. I remember thinking immediately that I was in good hands.

7: Music, Mead and Medicine

Opening my business post one morning I came upon a most unusual product enquiry. The handwritten letter was scrawled on headed notepaper that identified the sender as 'Maurice K. Bouette, Maker of Violins, Violas and Cellos'. A world-renowned instrument maker, Mr Bouette wanted to know if I could supply him with a quantity of propolis, going on to explain that this was one of the ingredients that went to make up a special wood varnish that had traditionally been used over the centuries to enhance the tonal quality of stringed instruments such as violins and violas by helping to add extra resonance. Its special properties in this respect were said to have first been discovered and developed by none other than Antonio Stradivari, most famous of all violin makers, who treated his now almost priceless instruments with a secret mixture that included propolis along with gum Arabic, honey and egg white. Mr Bouette, who was based in Nottinghamshire, where he founded and directed the Newark School of Violin Making, was interested in experimenting with various different types of propolis, which, like honey itself, can be light, dark or even gingery in colour. At the same time, he also inquired about the possibility of buying some honey suitable for making mead – so maybe he also liked a rare old home-brewed tipple to relax him at the end of a hard day in his workshop!

It seems that it is not only the finer stringed instruments from which even sweeter music can be coaxed with a little help from the hive. At the stall I regularly used to run at the monthly Moseley Farmers' Market I was approached one day by a local music teacher who was after beeswax with which to form the mouthpieces of his class's didgeridoos, explaining that it helped to promote a tight seal between lip and mouthpiece. Along with the earlier mentioned use of propolis as an ingredient in the manufacture of certain dental products, these rare musical applications must rate as some of the more unlikely examples to be found among the wide range of uses to which honey and various other hive products can be put. Also included are everything from the manufacture of candles, furniture polish, soaps and cosmetics to the preparation of various natural medicines and medications.

As a former nurse, my wife, Mary, has always been particularly interested in the medicinal applications. When she first started nursing back in the early sixties honey was routinely used in the treatment of wounds and sores and was included, along with sugar, in the Pharmacopoeia – the official list of drugs and medications and their uses. With the development of antibiotics it became unfashionable but is now once again being quite widely used in hospitals where it has been found to have the added advantage of being effective against nasty hospital bugs such as MRSA that can become resistant to antibiotics, but not to honey.

The healing properties of both honey and sugar have been known for centuries. The Ancient Egyptians first described honey as an effective treatment for wounds 4,000 years ago, while in the fourth century BC Aristotle was recommending light honey as a salve for sore eyes. A few hundred years later a fellow Roman, Dioscorides, was prescribing it for ulcers. Modern studies have confirmed its efficacy in the treatment of burns, skin ulcers and wounds and also diarrhoea and other stomach complaints.

The way in which it works on wounds and sores is that, like sugar sprinkled onto the affected area, it helps to clean it and draw out the moisture, starving bacteria by dehydrating them. Honey, in addition, has other properties and ingredients that aid the healing process. This has to do with hydrogen peroxide, a natural antiseptic that is produced by a glucose enzyme contained in honey.

The reason why its use in hospitals came to be discontinued in recent years was because it had never been subjected to the rigorous research and trials now demanded by the worldwide health authorities before any drug or medication can be officially approved and licensed. A treatment based on what was regarded by many in the medical establishment as little more than an old wives' tale was not officially acceptable, even though it was known to work. To carry out the required research was prohibitively expensive and there was certainly no way that beekeepers, however keen to make more of their products, could afford to sponsor the process.

In this respect the breakthrough came in New Zealand with Manuka honey, which is produced by bees feeding on the flowers of the manuka bush. Manuka honey doesn't have the greatest flavour and bee farmers there were having difficult marketing it for general consumption. However, they managed to persuade the New Zealand government to help with the funding of a research programme that verified claims that the honey had a uniquely powerful antibacterial property that could be effective in treating both internal and external ailments. As well as promoting external healing it was found to be particularly effective against a specific strain of bacteria – helicobacter – that causes stomach complaints. As a result it was not only approved for use in hospitals but was also able to command a premium price on supermarket shelves.

Manuka remains the only honey to have been given an official stamp of approval by health authorities, with its own special UMF (Unique Manuka Factor) antibacterial strength rating. However, there is every reason to suppose that most honeys have healing properties. Although Mary wasn't allowed to use it in hospital in her latter years as a nurse she was always convinced that it worked and in one or two cases where she was looking after patients privately in their own homes she used it to treat bed sores with great success, simply smearing some of our own honey onto gauze and applying it to the sores. And, of course, honey's various medical and medicinal applications form an important part of the Bees Abroad beekeeping education programmes in Africa and other developing countries where regular medicines and antibiotics are costly and not always readily available.

It is not only the honey itself that has healing properties. Beeswax, too, can be used as an effective wound dressing and also as a non-greasy alternative to Vaseline, while propolis, dissolved in pure alcohol – or, if that's not available, vodka – has anti-fungal, anti-viral, anti-inflammatory and even anti-tumour properties that can reduce swelling. Again, Mary can vouch for its effectiveness in this respect from personal experience, having used it with some success to treat her father when, in his nineties, he developed a rectal tumour. It was decided that at his age surgery was not really an option, but the propolis-based tablets that Mary then suggested brought him considerable relief.

Of all hive products it is royal jelly for which the most extravagant health and beauty claims have been made, largely because of the publicity generated on its behalf by the late and extremely colourful romantic novelist Dame Barbara Cartland. Once dubbed 'The First Lady of Nutrition', Dame Barbara's extraordinarily prolific literary output of a world record 723 books included one entitled *The Magic of Honey* in which, among other things, she suggested that royal jelly could help you stay looking younger longer. She based this on the fact that queen bees, which are fed exclusively on royal jelly, can live for up to four or five years while worker bees only survive for forty or fifty days. She also quoted an American university study which found that chickens fed royal jelly laid twice as many eggs as normal while older chickens past the normal laying age started laying again. Citing all this as persuasive if not conclusive proof of royal jelly's power of rejuvenation, she herself consumed it regularly and enthusiastically until her death at the age of 98.

It is certainly true that royal jelly, a milky white substance produced in the pharyngeal glands of worker bees, is rich in vitamins, enzymes, hormones and amino acids as well as antibacterial and antiviral agents. And as nutritional experts Dr James Balch and his wife Phyllis claimed in their book *Prescriptions for Nutritional Healing*, there is evidence to suggest that it can help with bronchial asthma, liver disease, bone fractures and skin disorders. But whether it is quite the elixir of youth that Barbara Cartland claimed is questionable – although she herself certainly appeared to thrive on it, remaining energetic enough to continue churning out books into her nineties while at the same time maintaining a highly glamorous image right to the end, always dressed up to the nines in what became her trademark pink.

In Kenya, much of Bees Abroad's training effort is now focused on encouraging our various beekeeping groups to develop a full range of value-added hive products. The broader, long-term aim there is to create sustainable businesses capable of providing people with desperately needed employment and income all year round, even during those long periods of drought when, with nectar sources inevitably reduced, the honey harvest itself is often as poor as that of crops in general.

 90

This is where beeswax, especially, can really come into its own as far as African beekeepers are concerned. It doesn't rot or melt, even in extreme heat, nor is it susceptible to attack from rodents, so it can easily be stored over quite long periods for use in other products when there is not much honey to sell. In the past, many African beekeepers just tended to throw the wax away most of the time. Now they are learning that far from being a waste product it is actually a valuable by-product that can be used to make candles, creams and cosmetics, all items for which there is a ready local market.

As with so much of the sort of low-level cottage industry that you find in the poorer parts of Africa, the manufacturing processes involve a fair amount of improvisation as well as the incorporation of readily and sometimes freely available natural ingredients wherever possible. Candles, for instance, are often moulded in disposable paper or plastic drinking cups, while the wicks are fashioned from strands of cotton salvaged from old mop heads.

Skin creams and lip balms are made by mixing beeswax with vegetable oils from plants that people can grow and process themselves, such as avocados, sunflowers, maize and olives, and are often scented with natural fragrances from home-grown or wild herbs. Such products are much in demand in conditions where constant exposure to hot sun dries out the skin and cracks the lips, where hard manual labour leaves hands roughened and calloused and where walking everywhere barefoot leads to sore soles and heels. The inclusion of oil extracted from a plant known as neem, commonplace in Africa, adds anti-septic, anti-bacterial properties, ideal for an ointment that can be applied to childhood cuts and grazes. It also acts as an effective insect repellent. Add oil of wintergreen and you have an anti-inflammatory cream.

The full range of successful value-added hive products that Bees Abroad has been helping to introduce includes everything from candy bars to shampoo. Candy bars are made from honey mixed with milk powder and peanut butter and flavoured with nuts, dried fruit and even coffee, while the addition of a few teaspoonfuls of honey to a basic shampoo turns it into the equivalent of a two-in-one shampoo-and-conditioner. This particular product has gone down especially well with everybody. Both the men and the women tend to take great pride in their hair and right from the start they were thrilled to bits with the honey shampoo, which does seem to provide extra shine! And it's so easy to produce. Our beekeepers simply buy large 5ltr wholesale containers of cheap shampoo and then, having added the honey, sell it on in small bottles at a handsome profit.

In trying to encourage this sort of diversity we have been working in close co-operation with the National Beekeeping Station in Nairobi and, in particular, with officer-in-charge Grace Asiko, and station trainer Winnie Kurgat. The station boasts a wealth of expertise and experience not only in the making of locally-marketable products using honey and beeswax along with various other readily available natural ingredients, but also with regard to such practical matters as sourcing supplies of suitable containers. As part of a project funded by a donation from regular Bees Abroad supporters Nick and Julia Bion, Winnie has been out conducting training courses for all our various beekeeping groups around the country, helped enormously by our own volunteer in-country trainer, David Njuguna. As well as taking on the responsibility of making all the necessary arrangements involved in actually organising the courses, including the supply of sufficient quantities of beeswax with which to work, David has also done much to make the groups fully aware of the various support services available to individuals and to small and medium-sized business enterprises, including start-up loans from local microfinance institutions such as the Equity Bank.

On one of our most recent trips to Kenya we also got together with an existing NGO, Desert Edge, which is based at Nanuki near the foot of Mt Kenya. Director Susie Wren and her team there are engaged in looking at encouraging bio-diversity generally in the region and, among other things, they are supporting a number of beekeeping groups in the area around Lakepia and Samburu, so there is an obvious synergy between Desert Edge and Bees Abroad. They are equally enthusiastic about the whole idea of promoting beekeeping and, together, we have been attempting to get some funding from the Department For International Development (DFID).

In the meantime, we are already busy working on developing the packaging, labelling and marketing of the various products. Having dreamed up and registered what we modestly think is a nicely appropriate and rather clever, catchy brand name – Bee Kind – we have had some specimen

Winnie Kurgat teaching members of a women's group how to make candles

Mary and me on a visit to the National Beekeeping Station in Nairobi with (l to r) Blaise Okinyi, officer-in-charge Grace Asiko and David Njuguna

Label design for Bee Kind products

snap-top tins produced and, with the help of an artist friend named Sally Fletcher Pemberton, have been experimenting with various label designs that incorporate the Kenyan national colours of red, green and gold.

There can be little doubt that bee farming, even on a very small scale, has the potential to be enormously beneficial to the poor of Africa. It doesn't require land, it doesn't require much in the way of initial investment and it costs nothing to feed the livestock because there is something out there called nectar that comes free. All this is recognised by the people themselves, especially the womenfolk who make up most of our beekeeping groups, seeing it as an ideal and relatively simple way for them to supplement the family income. In a country where people are accustomed to living from hand-to-mouth, the greatest problem lies in educating them into more businesslike, long-term thinking so that they can build a sustainable enterprise. They tend to be very laid back and their natural inclination is simply to sell any surplus honey they produce at the roadside as soon as it is harvested – and not always for the best price. Gradually, however, with the help of the National Beekeeping Centre, Desert Edge and other organisations, Bees Abroad is getting the message across.

8: Crisis? What Crisis?

Between 1980 and 1986 I was, successively, Vice-Chairman, Chairman and then Immediate Past Chairman of the UK Bee Farmers Association, having previously been Chairman of both the Warwickshire Beekeepers Association and its Leamington and Warwick branch. And when my six-year term of office with the Bee Farmers Association ended I received a letter from long-serving General Secretary A.D. 'Des' Winslow thanking me for my efforts throughout a critical period during which, as he put it: "You have had to deal with more problems than any previous Chairman in my experience."

These problems were partly internal, with things getting off to a rather difficult start when the new General Secretary, who had just taken over following Winslow's retirement, suddenly vanished without warning and completely without trace, taking vital Association records with him. It turned out that his disappearance had to do with various upheavals in his personal life. With the help of some of our local members north of the border we eventually tracked him down in Scotland and managed to retrieve most of our records along with the office typewriter, but we were still left without a General Secretary. In the end, Des Winslow kindly agreed to come out of retirement and hold the fort until such time as we could find a replacement.

Apart from this little local difficulty, there was the wider and much more serious concern of what to do about the rapidly mounting threat to beekeeping posed by an upsurge in the spraying of agricultural pesticides and insecticides. Reflecting a fundamental change in modern farming methods and the endless drive for ever greater crop yields, this had reached a new peak by the early 1980s with the blanket spraying of chemicals, some of which were highly dangerous to bees. The situation was made even worse by the trend at that time towards aerial spraying from helicopters or light aircraft. Farmers favoured this method because it was quicker and easier

Wearing my chain of office as Chairman of the UK Bee Farmers Association the second time around

and avoided damage to crops caused by driving tractor-drawn sprayers through the fields. But, of course, spraying from the air could not be quite so tightly targeted with the result that there was often quite widespread fallout.

The aerial spraying contractors insisted that they were always aware of the exact location of hives in areas where they were working and that they were careful to avoid getting too close to them. But on one occasion when I spotted a helicopter flying low and spraying over fields near one of my sites I tracked it back to where it landed and confronted the pilot. He claimed to know where my hives were, but when I pressed him it was pretty obvious that he hadn't actually got a clue.

Beekeepers at the time were suffering vast losses left, right and centre that were mostly attributable, either directly or indirectly, to the effects of spraying. The Ministry of Agriculture (now DEFRA) and other relevant authorities were all aware of the growing problem and of the need to enforce a strict licensing system to control the development and use of chemical pesticides and insecticides that were potentially harmful to the wider environment in general and to bees in particular. Every year the Ministry would organise a special Bees Meeting attended by its own representatives, the UK Bee Farmers Association and other beekeeping organisations, the NFU, the manufacturers and suppliers of sprays and the National Association of

Agricultural Contractors, including spraying contractors. And every year the main topic of discussion would be the damage being done to honey bees by certain sprays. However, with new products coming onto the market all the time the process of identifying those that were dangerous and then getting them removed from the official approved list was slow and cumbersome. It involved those beekeepers who believed that they had suffered spray damage having to collect and send off samples of dead bees to be analysed in Ministry laboratories, along with a full report containing details of the spray site. At the same time, we faced strong resistance from the big chemical companies and suppliers, with all their financial muscle, power and influence.

The UK Bee Farmers Association usually had two representatives at the Bees Meeting – the Chairman along with the committee member responsible for pesticides and insecticides. In my time that was Ken Beevor. It got to the point one year when Ken and I felt we really had to push hard for a really effective crackdown on the use of chemical sprays and we agreed beforehand to adopt a good cop/bad cop approach. I was supposed to be the good cop, all gentle persuasion, but when it came to the crunch I forgot all about that and found myself turning bad! I challenged the other delegates head on, pointing out that while they all had guaranteed salaries, bee farmers did not, and that if those bee farmers were suddenly to lose a third or more of their income because of somebody else's activities, as had been happening in some cases as a result of indiscriminate chemical spraying, then it was certainly unfair if not downright immoral. I urged them to think about that and to remind themselves that we, as the bee farmers' representative body, had been very reasonable up to that point and had not gone to the Press, despite having enough ammunition to give them all a hard time, both as official authorities who were failing in their duty to provide adequate environmental controls and as leading members of a chemical insecticides and pesticides industry that seemed to put profit before everything else.

Ken and I certainly had a bit of fun that day and at the end of my little outburst there was total silence in the room. But it served its purpose and over the next few years we did gradually manage to get a lot of the really damaging products removed from the approved list issued by DEFRA and taken off market, to be replaced by ones that the chemical companies claimed were safe. Being rather cynical, I suspected that they could have developed the less harmful products at any time but preferred to carry on with the ones they already had simply because it was cheaper and more profitable to do so.

Happily – and partly, I like to think, as a result of our campaign – the situation today is vastly improved in that respect and there are now hardly any cases of direct spray damage, apart from odd instances where, for instance, a pest control operator has sprayed a wild nest in a loft or chimney after which farmed bees have come in to rob the remaining store of honey that will have been contaminated. And yet the papers have recently been full of sensational stories about a major developing worldwide beekeeping crisis, with reports of colonies everywhere being decimated. This has led to scaremongering talk of a catastrophic impact on the balance of nature and even a long-term threat to life on Earth through a breakdown of pollination. Albert Einstein's other famous theory – that if honeybees were ever to become extinct mankind would be gone four years later – is once again being aired.

So what is the truth? What is causing the current problem and just how serious is it?

Some of the statistics are undoubtedly rather alarming, especially those coming out of America, where the total number of active hives has almost halved since 1980 and where the term Colony Collapse Disorder (CCD) first came to be used in late 2006 to describe a sudden and phenomenal increase in the number of hives left empty by disappearing colonies, with beekeepers reporting widespread losses of between 30% and 90%. However, the situation in Europe and the UK is not nearly so extreme and although it is true that losses generally have been much higher than usual in recent years, with a few isolated reports of CCD-type incidents, there are readily identifiable reasons for this – firstly the indiscriminate use of pesticides and then, when that was controlled, the arrival and rapid spread of the Varroa mite.

I certainly don't subscribe to the idea that what we are witnessing is actually the start of some mysterious new epidemic of biblical proportions that is going to sweep the globe and wipe out the bee population altogether. We need to keep things in perspective. Beekeepers generally have always routinely expected to suffer winter losses of up to 10% and although that average figure has certainly been creeping up fairly steadily in recent years in Europe and elsewhere to nearer 20%, no other country has experienced devastation on anything like the level that is being reported from America.

I suspect that particular management and environmental factors may help to account at least in part for what has been happening in the USA. Commercial bee farming there tends to be organised on a much more industrial scale than it is over here, with vast articulated truckloads of bees being transported over huge distances to pollinate almond and fruit orchards far and wide, from Florida to California. Many bee farmers are actually more interested in fulfilling pollination contracts than in producing honey – I met one who told me that he could exist very comfortably on the fees from just three major contracts – and perhaps because of this priority the conditions under which the bees are moved around are often far from ideal.

That same American beekeeper told me that he didn't have his own trucks – he simply employed a haulage contractor to do the transportation. He went on to explain that literally hundreds of hives would be forklifted onto trucks that would then be on the road for up to three days and nights on the longer trips. During the journey the individual hives would be left open, but with a micromesh net over the entire cargo. To my mind, the stress on the bees of being driven throughout the heat of the day, trapped under the micromesh when they would normally have been out foraging, must be immense. And stressed bees, just like stressed human beings, are likely to be out of condition and more susceptible to disease, their resistance having been weakened. The farmer agreed that his bees were not always in great shape when they finally arrived at their destination, but insisted that they soon "picked up". He also admitted that there would be quite a few casualties along the way.

How many did he mean by "quite a few", I asked?

"Only the odd barrelful or two," he replied with a shrug.

I was horrified. A honey barrel is bigger than a full-sized water butt, standing chest high and much too wide for a man to get his arms around it,

Mass migration – how bees are transported to fulfil pollination contracts in the US

so we're talking thousands, if not tens of thousands, of dead bees. And those would just be the ones that were found on the floor of the truck or caught up in the nets at the back. Thousands more would probably have been dead in the hives.

As well as the stress and disorientation caused by regular long distance transportation of colonies, there are other factors involved in American beekeeping and pollination practices that I feel could be contributing to the losses they are suffering there. For one thing, the orchards often cover vast acreages, with virtually no other nectar or pollen source available other than the blossom of the particular trees that are being pollinated. In California, the almond orchards that account for 80% of the world's total production cover no less than 600,000 acres! But bees, like most livestock, naturally tend to thrive on a mixed diet. When I moved my bees into the Kent orchards they wouldn't just work the apple and pear blossom, but would also forage among the dandelions and wild flowers growing in between the rows of trees as well as other nearby hedge blossom. Some of those American orchards, the almond orchards in particular, stretch for miles, as far as the eye can see in every direction, with virtually no other blossom of any sort to offer the bees a bit of variety.

Apart from that, there is also a suspicion that the American bee population overall may have been genetically weakened as a result of beekeepers there regularly re-stocking with new queens bought from the same small group of breeders, meaning that the gene pool has become too small.

One way and another it seems to me that commercial beekeepers in

99

America do tend to push their bees very hard – and if you push nature too far it has a habit of turning round to bite you. However, although the factors mentioned above may have contributed to the overall losses in America, the exact cause of true CCD – where whole colonies simply disappear without trace, leaving behind no dead bees on which to carry out post mortems – remains a worrying mystery.

So far, where there have been instances of sudden, severe and initially unexplained CCD-type losses in the UK and Europe, a specific cause has, in the end, nearly always been positively identified. For example, a series of outbreaks in France, Italy and Germany was eventually traced back to a particular seed dressing used on maize that had contaminated the growing plant itself, killing the bees that eventually came to feed on it. The company responsible claimed that this was a one-off and rectified the problem fairly promptly.

On a more mundane level, although the loss of several hives, especially by a small scale hobby beekeeper, may all too readily be cited as another case of CCD given the current scare, my long experience suggests that it is more likely to be attributable to such things as poor management on the part of individual beekeepers – including failure to take adequate precautions against Varroa and to replace old queens that have then failed to lay in the spring – localised weather or environmental conditions or a combination of several of these factors. It is not necessarily another sign that we are on the brink of Armageddon.

It is important to bear in mind that there have been problems with disease

The varroa mite – public enemy No 1 in the beekeeping world

and mite infestation, some of them very severe, ever since people first started keeping bees. Isle of Wight Disease, also known as Acarine Disease, devastated stocks in the early part of the 20th century. Foul Brood – both the American (AFB) and European (EFB) strains – then became a major threat worldwide. And, since the early '90s, the Varroa mite has become an even deadlier perennial menace.

Although they can never be totally eradicated, all these diseases and infestations can be controlled with careful management and constant vigilance. But that does involve a lot of extra work. Gone are the days when hobby beekeepers only had to check their hives thoroughly two or three times a year. Regular weekly visits, especially during the season, are now pretty much essential. That perhaps helps to explain why membership of the British Beekeepers Association plummeted from a peak of 32,000 in 1970 to just 10,000 in 2007. People simply became discouraged.

However, it's not all bad news. Although annual bee losses in the UK, as recorded by the British Beekeepers Association, continue to run at between 15-20%, double the 7-10% that used to be considered the acceptable norm, the decline in membership of the Association has not just been halted but has actually been quite dramatically reversed in the last five years, with numbers now back up to 23,000. This is attributed largely to renewed interest in beekeeping sparked by all the publicity about the so-called bee crisis. Along with this surge in BBKA membership, the number of hives registered in the UK has also doubled from 40,000 to well over 80,000 during the same period, with the total number of bees estimated to have risen from 23 billion to 48 billion.

All this is not to suggest that we have any reason to be complacent about a situation in which honeybees, like so many other animal, bird and insect species, are under increasing pressure from changes in the climate, the natural environment and, perhaps most importantly, modern farming methods. When it comes to boosting agricultural yields, we obviously have to be increasingly aware of the vital necessity of maintaining a balance between the immediate needs of mankind and the long-term future of the planet.

In particular, we have to maintain a very close watch on the development of all new pesticides, weed killers and what are now rather euphemistically known as 'plant control products'. Following our success in getting some of the more dangerous sprays removed from DEFRA's approved list in the '70s and '80s, we are now having to deal with a new generation of chemical products that have been developed to act systemically, being absorbed into the plant as it is growing so as to make it pest-resistant. The maize seed dressing mentioned earlier was just one example of this. Routinely tested only on adult bees, these products can be shown to be initially harmless. However, there is a suspicion that nectar and pollen from these plants, taken back to the hive, can have a detrimental effect on young, newly hatched bees, gradually destroying the colony from within, as it were. As with humans, adult bees are immune to problems that can be dangerous to babies and infants.

Thankfully, the indiscriminate chemical spraying of the '70s is a thing of the past. Greater environmental awareness has ensured that much tighter controls are in place. And yet beekeepers are still involved in an on-going battle to keep up with the big chemical companies, who are constantly developing new, ever more effective products. And that's not all. At one point a few years ago I had to move more than a hundred of my hives from their regular, well-established sites to different locations after a trial site for genetically modified (GM) crops was established on farmland nearby at Harbury. The problem with this was that the Honey Packers Association had already announced that it would not trade in honey that might have been contaminated with GM pollen, which meant that you couldn't have hives within three miles of any GM crop. Suddenly having to move the bees around involved me in a lot of extra work and expense and was also potentially harmful to the bees themselves. I and other local beekeepers led a public protest against the trials and I even considered taking legal action to get compensation until I realised that the chances were that, in the end, I would simply be throwing good money after bad.

When it comes to CCD, the suspicion remains that some sort of spray or plant protection product is to blame for the bees' disappearance. But without dead bees to examine, it is obviously impossible to ascertain the exact cause of death – or even to establish if an environmental 'crime' has actually been committed.

One theory is that the bees' sense of direction and their homing instinct has been corrupted in some way. It has occurred to me that since some basic insect sprays attack the target's nervous system – just think of how flies spin round and round, out of control, when sprayed with a household fly killer – then maybe the bees are somehow being affected in the same sort of way. That would account for the manner in which they just vanish from the hives, leaving them mysteriously empty, rather like the Marie Celeste.

Personally, I have never experienced anything quite like CCD. My worst losses – over 50% in a single season back in the mid '70s – resulted from Dutch elm disease. That terrible blight was especially widespread in Warwickshire, where there were probably more elms than in any other English county. In an effort to survive, the trees were pumping up a dark brown sap that oozed out of the trunks through the holes bored by the bark beetles that spread the fungal disease. And because this was happening at the end of a long, dry summer, with precious little natural nectar left, the trees were smothered in insects, including bees, bumble bees, wasps and butterflies, all feeding on this sweet sap. The bees were bringing it back and putting it in the combs, producing a dark, bitter honey that was not only just about inedible but which also proved fatal to the young bees that were fed on it, leading to the death of the colony over the winter.

One rather unexpected aspect of the recent revival of interest in beekeeping has been the significant increase in the number of urban beekeepers. We still tend to think of beekeeping as being primarily a country pursuit and yet the honey produced in suburban and even inner city areas is often of a very high quality, thanks to the wide variety of nectar sources available in parks, gardens, window boxes and even alongside railway lines, places where the flowers and shrubs have the added advantage of being free from agricultural sprays.

At the National Honey Show in 2011 the award for Best Honey From Inside The M25 went to a Mr Dale Gibson, whose Bermondsey Street Honey is produced from hives on the rooftop of his home, four storeys above a busy East End street. Steve Benbow, author of a new book entitled *The Urban Beekeeper*, also started off in Bermondsey and now has hives on top of the Tate Modern and Tate Britain art galleries, Fortnum & Mason and the National Gallery and supplies honey to the likes of the Savoy, Harvey Nichols and Harrods.

Right at the very top end of the social scale, so to speak, there are now hives at Buckingham Palace, where bees foraging around the 39-acre gardens have access to no less than 600 varieties of trees and plants and 350 different wildflowers. The first two hives were set up there in April 2009, producing 83 jars of clear and reportedly very fine multiflora honey for the royal kitchens in the first season. Two more hives were added the following year, pushing production up to 160 jars and beekeeper John Chapple, the London Beekeepers Association chairman who was already looking after 40-odd hives in royal parks across London before being brought in oversee the Buckingham Palace project, was then invited to set up two hives at Clarence House, Prince Charles' London residence.

I am proud to say that my own Fosse Way honey, as well as being served at The Ritz in Piccadilly for a time, has also found favour over the years with several different members of the royal family. The Duke of Edinburgh, the Duke of Kent, the Duchess of Gloucester and Prince Andrew have all visited the Fosse Way Honey stall in the Food Hall at the Royal Show at various times, all of them showing a genuine interest in beekeeping. Prince Andrew, in particular, turned out to be very knowledgeable. He stayed chatting longer than the organisers had anticipated, ignoring the efforts of the stewards to move him along. He asked about the state of beekeeping in the UK, how the weather and other factors were affecting it and how I was managing to deal with the problem of Varroa. That was something about which he was clearly very well clued up.

As he was saying goodbye, I asked him whether his daughters, Princesses Beatrice and Eugenie, liked honey.

"Oh, yes!" he replied enthusiastically. "They love it."

So I gave him a few jars in a carrier bag, which he passed to his equerry. Not long afterwards I got a charming letter from Clarence House, thanking me for the honey and adding that it had been much enjoyed.

I got an even more emphatic gesture of approval from Crown Prince Jagar Abdullah of Kuwait. He, too, visited the stall at the Royal Show and, having noticed that I had won an award or two as an exhibitor that year,

Prince Andrew proved very knowledgeable about Varroa and other beekeeping problems when he visited my stand at the Royal Show. Other Royals I met there over the years included Prince Philip and the Duke of Kent, both of whom showed a real interest in beekeeping

asked if he could have a taste. He liked it so much that he put in an order on the spot and from then on, every time his stocks ran low, an aide would be despatched to Deppers Bridge in a vast chauffeur-driven limousine to pick up fresh supplies that would be flown out to him in Kuwait.

A regular celebrity visitor behind the scenes at the Royal Show every year, and someone whom I got to know quite well as a result, was the late Norman Painting, the actor who played the part of Phil Archer in *The Archers* for more than sixty years until his death in 2009. Despite a lifetime spent portraying a fictional character who had become something of a national institution over all those years, he could walk around in public completely unrecognised because being a radio rather than a television soap star meant that his face remained unfamiliar. And as he himself always used to say rather apologetically, he didn't actually look anything like people imagined

Norman Painting, who played Phil Archer in The Archers for more than 60 years, was a regular at the Royal Show. He hated it when people got confused and addressed him as Phil instead of Norman

Phil to be from listening to him on the radio for so long. But that voice was unmistakable and as soon as you got into conversation with him there was this awful compunction to address him as Phil rather than Norman, which he hated. You had to be on your guard or it would slip out and you would notice him visibly wincing.

Underneath his rather urbane, thespian manner Norman was a genuine countryman and a keen gardener who was also interested in beekeeping, although he never actually had any hives of his own in the large garden of his village home on the Warwickshire/Oxfordshire border, not far from where I am based in Deppers Bridge. He used to visit the Royal Show every year and made a habit of always popping into the beekeeping section's private canteen area for a cup of tea and a chat. I think he regarded it as a bit of a haven from the hustle and bustle of the showground. He always wanted to know what was going on in the beekeeping world and the Royal Show generally. At the time, he was writing some of the scripts for *The Archers* as well as starring in it and I was told later by actress Patricia Gallimore, who plays the part of Pat Archer and whom I met when she visited the Fosse Way Honey stall at Stratford's Plough and Plate Fair, that he was probably on the lookout for storylines. Looking back, I should probably have made more of an effort to encourage the idea of him introducing a beekeeping plotline as a way of highlighting the problems faced by bee farmers struggling to make a living in a modern agricultural environment. There were certainly times when we felt we had plenty to protest about.

9: A Buzz of Protest

It was strictly in the line of duty as an official representative of the UK Bee Farmers Association that I found myself one day bumbling rather erratically around the streets of Brussels dressed as a giant bee. And I have it on the very best authority that, for a while at least, a photograph recording this event was prominently displayed on the walls of what was then the Ministry of Agriculture, Fisheries and Food.

It was 1993 and I was among hundreds of beekeepers from all over Europe who had converged on Brussels to take part in a demonstration outside the headquarters of the European Economic Community (EEC), which had just been integrated into an expanded European Union (EU), our aim being to secure EU financial support for commercial beekeeping through the Common Agricultural Policy. Agriculture ministers from all the member countries, including Gillian Shephard from the UK, were meeting to discuss the allocation of CAP subsidies and we wanted to make sure that beekeeping was not overlooked.

There were half-a-dozen of us in the UK contingent, five dressed up in beekeeper's protective gear, carrying smokers and waving Union Jacks, and me in the bee costume that included a striped sweater, black tights and a bee's head hood. We had gone over by car and ferry and first made our way to the NFU headquarters in Brussels, where we changed into our outfits. We then walked through the town to join the main parade that was to march on the EU building.

Thanks to my eye-catching costume I soon found myself the centre of much amused attention, with passers-by waving and shouting encouragement along with the odd bit of mild abuse. Our group was a little late joining the parade so that by the time we arrived the others were already lined up and as we walked down the line to take our place at the back, members of the other national delegations kept breaking ranks and running across to put their arms round me and have photographs taken of us together.

The parade, once it got going, was a very jolly, noisy, good-natured affair. The members of the Basque delegation, in particular, were in party mood. They had turned up with empty 28lb honey tins that they hung upside down around their necks and used as drums, creating quite a din that echoed off the buildings on each side of the street as we marched along. The Belgian police were out in force, dressed in full riot gear, with barbed wire barriers blocking off side roads in case things got out of control! However, these rather fearsome looking policemen soon realized that we didn't pose a major threat after we presented them with miniature jars of honey and the atmosphere became very relaxed.

A street right next door to the EU building had been closed to traffic and along each side the various national delegations had set up stalls from which they were distributing literature and a selection of honeys and hive products to both the general public and to the EU officials and Ministers of Agriculture who came out to meet us, including Gillian Shephard.

By then I was not only rather hot and sweaty in my bee costume – I was also ever so slightly tipsy. Mellow, shall we say! This was thanks to the generous hospitality of the Basque delegation who, as well as their makeshift drums, had also come armed with a plentiful supply of wine with which they kept the rest of us liberally refreshed. They seemed to take particular delight in repeatedly getting me to remove my bee's head hood to take yet another swig. The combination of the wine and the fact that I was having difficulty seeing exactly where I was going through the narrow eyeholes cut in my hood meant that I was a trifle unsteady on my feet as I stepped forward to meet Mrs Shephard. However, I'm pleased to say that it all passed off very smoothly and I didn't disgrace myself in any way.

The following year I met up with Mrs Shephard again, this time at the Royal Show at Stoneleigh, where, as usual, Fosse Way Honey had a stall in the Food Hall. Knowing that she was going to be visiting the honey section, I took along one of the photographs that had been taken of her with our group in Brussels and when one of her aides brought her over to my stall and introduced us I showed her the picture and asked her if she remembered the occasion.

Me in my bee costume – getting approval from the dog, waving the flag and meeting Minister of Agriculture Gillian Shephard

"Oh yes!" she replied, laughing. "As it happens, we've got a copy of this same photograph on the wall at the Ministry."

"Well, I'm the guy in the bee costume," I explained. "Would you sign the picture for me?"

"Of course, " she said. "Have you got a pen?"

I would like to be able to say that our Brussels demonstration was an unqualified success. However, although it did indeed achieve the aim of getting the EU to agree that beekeeping should be recognized as a separate sector of agriculture, eligible for its own subsidy as part of the CAP, we have always felt short-changed by the British government, which, we claim, has effectively stolen our EU money ever since then by simply using it to help fund existing DEFRA beekeeping advisory and inspection services rather than passing it on directly to commercial bee farmers, as was the EU's intention in our view.

It is a complicated situation. Under the terms of the CAP agreement, the EU subsidy was supposed to be matched by an equal amount of funding from each national government. But the British government's view was that as DEFRA was already putting money into beekeeping through the Food and Environment Research Agency (FERA) and the National Bee Unit (NBU), it didn't need to make a further contribution. So instead of going directly to commercial bee farmers, the subsidy is simply absorbed by FERA and used to fund the NBU.

The end result of all this is that commercial bee farmers are no better off than they were before. As we have always understood it, the EU money was supposed to be for three main purposes: to assist in the treatment of bees against Varroa by subsidising the cost of anti-Varroa products and treatment; to contribute towards the cost of moving hives around the country for the pollination of crops; and to help towards the cost of re-stocking hives left empty by colonies that fail to survive the winter. And yet British beekeepers get none of these benefits. Instead, what they are offered by DEFRA's Healthy Bees Plan, operated by FERA through the NBU, amounts to little more than an inspection service for foulbrood along with various educational and advisory services that are of no great value to commercial bee farmers since, as experienced professionals, they already pretty much know how to do their job. If they didn't, they would have gone under long ago.

The only people who do perhaps benefit are hobby beekeepers. And although every commercial bee farmer has probably been a hobby beekeeper to start with and is therefore likely to be in favour of support being provided for them wherever possible, the fact remains that the hobbyists are a transient community, with the British Beekeepers Association experiencing an annual turnover of up to one third of its 20,000 membership, thousands dropping out and thousands more coming in each year. That can only mean that there must be an awful lot of people out there who know a bit about beekeeping but aren't keeping bees, which doesn't seem to be a very efficient use of funding. And although those 20,000 hobbyists account for a third of all the honey produced in this country, most of it sold at the garden gate, the other two thirds is produced by around 350 commercial bee farmers. So, when it comes to long-term food security, effectively allocating the entire EU subsidy to part-timers again seems counter-productive.

The relative lack of encouragement and practical support for commercial bee farmers in this country probably accounts for the fact that the UK lags far behind the rest of Europe in honey production, producing just 10% of its own consumption as against 60% in many other countries. Because there is a lot of interaction between UK bee farmers and their counterparts in Europe, we are enviously aware of what they get in the way of subsidies. In Italy, for example, much of the EU money goes towards subsiding the costs of transporting hives around the country for crop pollination, with grants for equipment such as boom loaders that facilitate the loading of hives onto trucks. In France you can get grants to help you set up as a commercial beekeeper. But in this country there are no incentives whatsoever and, as we keep telling the government, there is a danger that commercial bee farmers will disappear altogether if that continues to be the case. The writing was already on the wall when R.O.B. Manley's Chiltern Honey Farm, once one of the biggest producers in the country, decided, quite literally, to pack it in, selling off all its hives and ceasing production altogether in order to concentrate exclusively on packing imported honey. Gale's of Marlborough and Rowse are among other major producers that have since gone the same way.

The lack of support is further reflected in the sad fact that not one of the country's agricultural colleges includes beekeeping in its full-time student courses any more. The Hampshire College of Agriculture at Sparsholt was the last one to do so. My old college, Hartpury, dropped beekeeping from its curriculum years ago, although, like one or two of the others, it does run occasional one-week courses for beginners, with a lecturer brought in specially to provide what amounts to little more than a general introduction to beekeeping.

To me, that's terrible indictment of our agricultural policy in this country. It goes back to the '70s and '80s when it was all push-push-push to raise crop yields, and farmers were encouraged to use chemical pesticides and fertilisers like there was no tomorrow, never mind the pollution and the environmental damage that was caused as a result. There was this frantic drive for more milk, more meat, more cereal crops and more vegetables, but honey production was not considered a priority and bees were forgotten. Beekeepers were seen as Cinderellas among the other sectors of agriculture, held back by Ministry bureaucrats in the roles of the Ugly Sisters. And yet that was very short sighted because apart from anything else, it ignored the value of bees as pollinators, not just of fruit trees, but also of many other crops. In that respect, it is interesting to note that the decline in honey production has gone hand-in-hand with the decline in commercial fruit production in this country, with many orchards being grubbed out and growers going out

As pollinators, bees are a vital link in our integrated food chain

of business in the face of competition from cheaper foreign imports. Most people know that you need bees to pollinate fruit trees, but not everybody is quite so well aware that they are also required for everything from beans to brassicas.

The lack of urgency shown by DEFRA and its agencies in helping to combat the threat of Varroa is another specific area in which commercial bee farmers feel they have been badly let down. If anything, plodding Whitehall bureaucracy and red tape have added to the problem by restricting access to proven effective treatments.

Varroa first arrived in this country from the Continent in 1992. The water barrier provided by the English Channel should have saved us in the same way that it protected us from rabies, but it didn't. The Varroa mite most probably came in on illegally imported bees. I made what was only a slightly tongue-in-cheek suggestion that DEFRA – or the Ministry of Agriculture and Fisheries as it was then – should have sued Customs and Excise for dereliction of duty in allowing Varroa into the country and that any damages awarded as a result of a successful prosecution should have gone towards subsiding treatment!

Once the invasion was confirmed, the National Bee Unit's initial response had a whiff of Dad's Army about it. We knew that an effective treatment for controlling Varroa was widely available in Europe, having been successfully trialed in France. But because it hadn't been officially licensed here by the Veterinary Medicines Directorate (VMD), an organization operating on behalf of DEFRA, we were not legally permitted to use it even though it

112

had been licensed in France and elsewhere in Europe. So much for cross-border EU co-operation! Because it cost the French manufacturers a lot of money to go through the process of getting the product licensed here, they decided it wasn't worth bothering. From their point of view, the sums just didn't add up. Meanwhile, the NBU was suggesting that we puff tobacco smoke into the hives!

There were quite a lot of us who were not prepared to stand idly by, watching our livestock become deadstock, so we simply went out and brought in the banned product, a special solution with which you coated wooden strips that were then inserted into the hives. We knew all about it in advance because we were in touch with the French bee farmers who had tested it and had found it to be effective. And we found a way of getting it here by a devious route via the Canary Islands and Spain. Several of us in the Midlands area alone were using it and our bees weren't in bad condition, which seemed to confirm that it really did work.

Later, after Varroa had spread across the Atlantic to Canada and the USA, a Canadian company came up with a simplified and much more convenient product that involved plastic rather than wooden strips, already impregnated with the anti-Varroa solution. This was still then technically illegal in this country – and somebody was actually taken to court for supplying the strips. I myself was buying them, but not supplying them, although I was happy to tell anybody who wanted to know exactly where they could get hold of them. After all, it is beekeepers who are responsible for their livestock, not any civil servant or politician. I accept that the authorities have a responsibility to see that you're not doing anything that might endanger the public, but in this case it was pure red tape. The product had been approved and registered throughout Europe, where tests had proved that it was safe and effective. And, of course, in the end it was approved and registered here and the plastic strips became readily available. It just took much longer than it should have done for the authorities here to give it the all clear at a time when beekeepers were desperate to get hold of an effective treatment for Varroa as quickly as possible.

We're still having problems in this respect. Inevitably, Varroa has gradually developed a resistance to the earlier product contained in the strips so that

113

they are no longer working quite as well as they did. To combat this, an alternative product has now been developed in Europe which, when used in rotation with the original one, ensures that you can keep on top of the problem. But, strictly speaking, you can only get it here if you first obtain a prescription from a vet. And the vet isn't supposed to give out a prescription unless he has examined the affected bees and diagnosed the problem.

The trouble with that is that the average vet knows very little about bees. And apart from that, the process costs an arm and a leg, as a friend of mine in Scotland found out when he decided to play by the rules. At the time of writing a new system is due to be introduced whereby you will be able to get the product without a prescription as long as you can prove that you are a so-called Suitably Qualified Person (SQP). But becoming a SQP involves going on a week's special course that supposedly enables you to understand bees, to identify infestations and to be able to give reasons why you want the product. Well, most professional beekeepers can do that anyway – they don't need to go on a course!

This is just the latest example of how we seem to have been held back all the time, first by the Ministry of Agriculture and Fisheries and then by DEFRA. In a way, they have contributed to our problems over the years rather than helping to solve them. Beekeeping may not be seen as 'big' agriculture – it's not like meat, milk or arable crop production – but, as pollinators, bees are a vital link in our integrated food chain and it is time that this was fully recognised in Whitehall and elsewhere.

10: Buzzing Off

Beekeeping on a commercial scale is a physically demanding occupation. It may not seem that way to those who tend to associate it with the traditional image of a straw-hatted figure quietly pottering about among a few hives under the apple trees at the bottom of his garden on a Sunday afternoon. But when you are a one-man band looking after 350 hives spread over two or three counties, with regular annual trips to the Derbyshire heather moors, the Kentish fruit orchards and the Worcestershire bean fields thrown in, plus all the heavy lifting that this involves, it can be surprisingly hard labour. And with advancing years comes the realisation that you are no longer able to work as long and as strong as you once used to do. Which is why, at the age of 65, I decided in 2005 that the time had come to sell Fosse Way Honey and retire.

Although I was beginning to slow down a bit the business was still going strong, but as there was nobody in the family that I could hand it on to I had no real option other than to sell up. And I was keenly aware of the need to find a buyer while Fosse Way was still a going concern and before it started showing signs of stagnation. I had known farmers in the same sort of situation who had hung on a little too long, gradually allowing their farms to run down. I had been to farm sales where an auctioneer would be selling everything off and you realised that the owner hadn't bought any new equipment for years and that what was left was all looking a bit dog-eared.

That sort of closing down sale would have been the quickest and easiest way of disposing of Fosse Way's assets, including the hives and all the processing equipment. However, that would have been to ignore the not inconsiderable value of the commercial aspect of the business – the network of shops and other outlets I had established where our honey was on sale, the long-standing pollination contracts and the goodwill of farmers who, for many years, had allowed my hives to be sited on their land. It therefore made a lot more sense to try to sell the business as a whole, but finding a suitable buyer was not going to be that simple or straightforward.

I didn't want to place adverts offering "an unusual opportunity to buy a fully equipped beekeeping business in the Midlands" for fear of being inundated with inquiries from every Tom, Dick and Harry who fancied trying his hand at beekeeping in much the same way that some people fall in love with the notion of taking over a country pub, without having any experience or any real idea of what the job actually entails. I wasn't sure that I would have the ability to sort out the serious candidates from the daydreamers. Apart from that, I was worried that if I announced in advance that I was selling up it would damage trade. Instead, I just quietly put the word about that I was starting to think about retiring and that I would be interested in talking to anyone who thought they might like to take over the business.

In the end it was one of the shopkeepers I had been supplying for some years who eventually approached me. Chris Atkins had a shop in The Parade in Leamington Spa but wanted to get out and try something different. He knew next to nothing about beekeeping at that point but was very enthusiastic and keen to learn, so I suggested that he should come and have a few days' 'work experience' with me to see if he was really up to the job. I then proceeded to give him a crash course in bee farming, showing him how everything basically worked and even taking him up to the moors. At the end of it he decided that he definitely wanted to go ahead and we negotiated a deal whereby I agreed to stay on as a consultant for two years after he took over the business, holding his hand, as it were, while he continued to learn the ropes. During that time I did my best to teach him everything I knew, also introducing him both to the farmers on whose land my hives were sited and the clients to whom I sold my honey.

Given that he started from scratch, Chris has done a remarkably good job and Fosse Way Honey continues to flourish, the business now operating from farm buildings just outside Brailes. I, meantime, have gone back to being a hobby beekeeper, albeit on quite a large and businesslike scale. I now have about sixty hives at home in Deppers Bridge and at various local farms, selling any surplus honey that I produce into the bulk trade. The terms of my deal with Chris included an agreement that I would not set

I still have quite a few hives at home in Deppers Bridge

up in business selling my own brand honey in competition to him for at least five years. That five-year period has since elapsed, but although, at the time of writing, I have no plans to start up on my own again there is a possibility that I could be tempted back into business in a small way if an apprenticeship scheme currently being considered by FERA and the UK Bee Farmers Association actually materialises.

The idea of the scheme has been prompted by the realisation that the majority of existing commercial bee farmers are, like me, getting a bit ancient and that a new generation of professionals needs to be encouraged. With none of the agricultural colleges any longer offering full-time beekeeping courses one possible option would be for the Bee Farmers Association to find some way of helping to fund apprenticeships for young would-be beekeepers with experienced professionals. If that idea comes to fruition I might well apply to take on an apprentice and train him up within a small new business. As it happens, I have someone in mind who I think would probably jump at such an opportunity, but at the moment it is still just a pipe dream.

Meanwhile, I seem to be just as busy as I ever was. When I'm not looking after my own hives I'm very happy to turn out and help friends with a day's beekeeping here and there if they happen to find themselves short-handed for some reason, returning many favours received over the years. I also look after twelve hives owned by my good friend Lino Pires, proprietor of The Butcher's Arms at Priors Hardwick in Warwickshire, plus four more that I set up for his daughter-in-law, Helen. The honey produced from these hives – up to three hundredweight a season – is either used in the restaurant's

With Lino Pires, his daughter-in-law Helen and a couple of their hives at The Butcher's Arms

kitchens or sold in aid of the Extra Mile charity fund-raising group that Helen supports or the Royal Marsden Hospital's Cancer Research Fund for which Lino has raised hundreds of thousands of pounds.

And then, of course, there is Bees Abroad. This continues to involve at least one annual trip to Kenya to check on existing projects and investigate possible new ones. Last time we went we were there for nearly five weeks. And as time goes on and Bees Abroad's activities around the country expand, there is also more and more administrative, organisational and fund-raising work to be done at this end, keeping both Mary and me increasingly occupied, especially since I also took on the job of Chairman of the Bees Abroad Management Committee. Not that we're complaining in any way. Our involvement with Bees Abroad has not only broadened our horizons in a very literal sense but has also given us the enormous personal satisfaction that comes with the success of an endeavour that is so clearly worthwhile and that rewards commitment with such encouragingly positive results.

Since my original introductory visit in 2006 we have set up a total of seven main projects, involving a number of different groups, nearly all now well established and mostly making good progress despite the three-year drought between 2008-2011 that had such a frustratingly detrimental effect on honey crops in East Africa generally.

The original project, at Nessuit, set up as part of the Nessuit Livestock, Beekeeping and Environmental Management (NELBEM) scheme, remains the flagship success, although, rather sadly in some ways, our formal commitment there has come to an end now that it is up and running and

118

Members of the women's group at NELBEM sealing a hive by daubing it with mud

largely self-sufficient. But we feel we have much to be proud of. Thanks largely to the tireless efforts there of our voluntary in-country trainer, David Njuguna, the number of families keeping bees has risen to over seventy, with a steady increase in the number of hives to a total of over one hundred.

The latest development there is that thirty members of the women's section have set up a separate self-managing group, with the specific aim of developing the production of hive products other than honey. This came about because the hives, the bees and the income from the honey mostly belong to the families – which, in effect, tends to mean the men – and the women wanted to find a way of independently earning a little extra money for themselves. They have already had great success in producing a hand cream that has proved very popular and which gives them a 50% profit over and above the cost of production and marketing. And with training from the National Beekeeping Station's Winnie Kurgat they are now working on producing a beeswax skin conditioner in a solid block form that requires only minimal packaging, thereby simplifying the production process and cutting costs.

At the same time, the tree nursery that Bees Abroad established partly to provide nectar sources continues to benefit members, while the group headquarters building that we also partly financed has proved a great asset, providing accommodation for meetings and training and also serving as a honey packing station. There is a constant demand for the honey, which fetches a relatively high price by Kenyan standards, and the group is in the enviable position of having a full order book.

At Machakos, where we continue to support the aims of Wings of Mercy, the

Mutini Self Help Group now numbers over sixty members and, impressively, holds meetings regularly once a week under the chairmanship of Wallace Ntiani and his committee. Bees Abroad recently supplied 1000 machine-made top bars, which helped to raise the number of hives to 46, three quarters of which are owned by women, who, just as at Nessuit and elsewhere among our projects, have enjoyed great and profitable success in producing and selling hand creams, skin conditioners, candles and candy bars.

The other group in the Machakos area, the Konza Agriculture Group at nearby Bondoni, has thirty members and so impressed a government agricultural officer during a recent official visit that he immediately ordered the provision of 28 new hives! In addition, Bees Abroad supplied both groups with the utensils needed to make the beeswax skin conditioner bars. Last time we were there we also undertook further training in the making of protective clothing from maize sacks and other locally available material. The training sessions turned out to be great fun, with the men, who often tend to be a bit stand-offish, suddenly and rather unexpectedly becoming extremely competitive, keen to show that they could make bee suits better and more quickly than the women.

The SMART project, centred on the Cheringani Hills, near the Ugandan border at Kitale, has been one of those worst hit by the recent three-year drought, with the field officers reporting difficulty in motivating their beekeeping groups in circumstances in which honey crops drop off due to the lack of nectar sources and the production of other food crops becomes an overriding priority. The focus of our most recent visit was to try to re-energise the groups now that the rains have returned and there are signs of a revival of enthusiasm.

The Kerio Valley project has moved ahead well, thanks largely to funds we have been able to make available from the £5,500 donation raised for Bees Abroad as a result of the sponsored run organised by the Trevor-Roberts School in North London. Using money from the group savings scheme, into which they each pay a weekly contribution, the twenty members of the Chepsigot Women's Group have managed to purchase a piece of land on which to set up their own group apiary and training centre.

At the last count they had succeeded in harvesting over 100kgs of honey in

Members of the Chepsigot women's group

their first season, all of which they were able to sell from roadside stalls for 250 Kenyan shillings per kilo, a very decent price by local standards. We have since supplied them with ten more locally made top bar hives, two new smokers and further beekeeping training manuals in Swahili. Following our last training visit, each of the members has made her own suit of protective clothing.

The group has established close links with the local Chepsigot Primary School, which in addition to providing routine primary education also runs a farm school where the pupils, including a number of blind and special needs children, are taught basic agricultural skills. Headmaster John Kronok and his Assistant Head have always been very helpful and supportive to the beekeeping group, allowing them to use classrooms for meetings outside school hours while also providing basic secretarial and accountancy advice. And they have now agreed to include beekeeping among the activities of the school's farm.

The twenty-five acres of land on which the school is located is incredibly fertile and we were amazed to be shown examples of how, in the course of a single year, 18-inch paw paw seedlings had grown into seven-foot-tall trees, laden with fruit. On our visit at the end of 2011 Mary and I, along with David Njuguna and fellow Bees Abroad volunteer Dave Bonner, who had joined us in Kenya on his way to visit projects in Uganda, went along to meet John Kronok in order to identify a suitable site at which to set up a training apiary, with an initial three hives donated by Bees Abroad.

Elsewhere in the Kerio Valley, Bees Abroad has also forged links with the Cheptebo Rural Development Centre. An agricultural training

121

establishment operating on a 50-acre demonstration farm, the Centre specialises in teaching farmers how to boost crop production and how best to manage livestock, mostly goats and cows, in semi-arid conditions.

This is an ideal location at which to promote the development of beekeeping, which is seen as having great potential not just in helping directly to reduce the high level of poverty in the Kerio Valley but also by making an important contribution to environmental conservation in the area by introducing tree planting as an essential part of the projects. Plans for the development of a training apiary at the Centre are now well advanced. While we were there in 2011 Dave Bonner and I helped farm manager Walter Rono to hang 'catcher' boxes – small hives baited with wax and lemon grass in order to attract swarms. We also presented Walter and his staff with seven sets of second-hand protective bee suits, generously donated by the National Beekeeping Unit in the UK, and agreed that Bees Abroad would supply four top bar hives.

During our stay in the Cheptebo area we also organised two days of training and demonstrations at the Centre, attended by twenty Bees Abroad project members from the surrounding area. They included ladies from both the Chepsigot and Sinyati Women's Groups who had walked a considerable distance from their villages deep in the bush at the other end of the valley in order to be there, a marvellously encouraging indication of their enthusiasm and rewarding confirmation for us that what Bees Abroad is trying to do is truly worthwhile.

The first day started with a demonstration of how to make candles, using wax melted over a charcoal fire, with cotton threads for wicks and paper cups for moulds. Next, we showed them how to make skin cream. We had run out of charcoal by this time so had to improvise by lighting a wood fire over which to melt the ingredients. Heating vegetable oils and beeswax to boiling point over an open fire probably wouldn't meet with EU Health and Safety regulations but in Africa you constantly have to make do with whatever comes to hand. Our students were very excited when we produced fifty containers of cream and got even more excited when we explained that each batch of fifty would yield a profit of 2,500Ksh – equivalent to about £18.

On Day 2, Winnie Kurgat gave a demonstration of how to make cough medicine using honey, garlic, ginger and lemon. The resulting concoction certainly cleared the sinuses! She followed this with a recipe for another medicinal compound for the relief of asthma and arthritis. This one featured honey and aloe vera and was a little more palatable than the cough mixture. Mary then showed how to make candy bars using honey, milk powder, coffee and chocolate; also bars of body lotion made from beeswax and scented herbs; and shampoo made from small amounts of ordinary shampoo mixed with honey to make the hair softer and shinier. As always, this seemed to go down especially well.

Before we left Cheptebo we were visited at the Centre by a delegation from another of our local Kerio Valley projects, the SUMAT Development Group. Previously known as the Rochoko Group, the name had to be changed because of confusion with another registered organisation. This go-ahead group now has fifteen members, each of whom pays a 50 Ksh membership fee, the money being used to buy equipment. With a quantity of top bars supplied by Bees Abroad they now have thirty hives and have applied for a community development trust fund grant to help them expand their activities further. As well as giving them demonstrations of how to make the usual variety of value-added hive products during their visit to the Cheptebo Centre, I also gave them some instruction on how to protect their hives from pests such as the honey badgers with which they had been having particular problems. Once again, they went away in a very happy, positive and hugely enthusiastic mood.

The Sinyati Women's Group, whose members made such an effort to attend the training sessions at Cheptebo, is another inspiring success story.

Me and David Njuguna
training at Rochoko

123

The group was formed by fourteen Masai women from a tiny village between Lake Boringo and Lake Bogoria, which, because of its remoteness, would not normally receive much help of any kind from other organisations. The village can be reached only by rough tracks through the bush that become an almost impassable quagmire when it rains heavily, as it did shortly before we visited during our stay in Cheptebo.

Our involvement initially came about through the efforts of group leader Caroline Lentupuru, a remarkable local woman who recently came to London to receive an international award in recognition of her campaigning work in schools and villages throughout the area, aimed specifically at stamping out the practice, still all-too-common in parts of Africa, of subjecting young girls between the ages of twelve and sixteen to female genital mutilation. At the same time, she has also been trying gently to discourage the idea of forcing girls into early marriage. Caroline wants girls to be able to continue with their schooling so that they will become more educated and self-reliant, which she hopes will, in turn, help to alleviate poverty by empowering women to generate extra income. She realised that beekeeping could help in this respect by giving women a measure of financial independence. During her two-week visit to the UK towards the end of 2011 she met MPs concerned with overseas development, stressing to them the point that government aid to developing countries could often be more effective when provided to smaller grass roots organisations such as Bees Abroad.

From the outset, our visit to Sinyati – Mary and I again accompanied by Dave Bonner as well as by David Njuguna – turned out to be an eventful experience, as exciting for us as it apparently was for our hostesses from the beekeeping group. The journey from the nearest town of Marigat – ten kilometres through the bush as the crow, or more likely the vulture, flies – took nearly two hours, owing to detours made necessary by the rains that had washed away parts of the track.

On our eventual arrival we were greeted by the members of the group, all of them colourfully dressed in traditional Masai style. A table and chairs had been set out halfway up a hill in the shade of a large acacia tree to serve as a classroom for our training session. But first we were served with a delicious

124

lunch of local fruit, stewed meat and vegetables, washed down with African tea. As we sat down to eat, it started to rain again but three of the ladies stood up to 'wave' the rain away. Apparently, only first-born females are able to do this. And, sure enough, the rain stopped almost immediately and the sun came out.

After lunch Mary gave a demonstration of how to make various beeswax products, including a skin cream with neem added as an insect repellent. The group then proudly took us to see their apiary from which, since we had helped them to set it up the previous year, had produced nearly 150 kg of honey for sale in the market at Marigat.

Me, Mary, Dave Bonner and David Njuguna with the Sinyati women's group, all of us dressed in traditional Masai shirts and dresses presented to us as gifts

Mary teaching members of the group

Our planned return for a second training session the following day had to be postponed because of further heavy overnight rain. However, when we did get back we were taken to see the fields in which the villagers had planted French beans, melons and maize bought with the small amount

of emergency aid that Mary and I had managed to raise through a local appeal back home in Southam after the villagers lost all their forty milking goats during a violent raid by the notorious Pokot tribe. This had taken place the previous year shortly after our initial visit to set up the beekeeping group there. The raiders had terrified everyone by spraying the village with machine gun fire before stealing the goats.

As soon as we heard about it we immediately launched an appeal through Southam's local parish church of St James and a got a wonderful response. So it was great to be able to report back that the money raised had been well spent.

Our other task on the return visit to Sinyati was to identify a suitable spot at which to set up a new training apiary, the existing one being situated a bit too close to the dirt track that led into the village, with the result that passers-by were being stung when the hives were being worked on. Because of this, the ladies had taken to doing their active beekeeping after dark.

We were very soon given a painful reminder of how aggressively defensive some African bees can be. Having identified a more suitable site, Dave Bonner and I went back to the existing one to collect some empty hives with which to give a demonstration of the baiting that is necessary to attract bees. As we approached we became aware of loud buzzing and arrived just in time to see a huge swarm emerge from one of the occupied hives. The swarm settled on a branch high up in a tree, too high to be collected, and as we tried to get close Dave got stung on the face. At that point the two of us decided to make a swift strategic withdrawal.

Once the swarm had calmed down a bit we ventured back into the apiary with a rather nervous helper to retrieve one of the supposedly empty hives. As Dave and the helper lifted the hive off the pole from which it was suspended and started carrying it out the increasingly twitchy assistant, eyeing the swarm nervously and obviously keen to get clear as quickly as possible, started rushing things. The hive banged against the gatepost of the apiary with a violent thud at which point a lot of angry wasps suddenly flew out and started attacking the pair of them. The assistant then panicked and made a run for it, dragging Dave behind him.

Fortunately, the wasps' nest was small and easily dealt with. Once cleaned and baited, the hive was re-hung in the apiary by two of the group's ladies wearing home-made protective suits. I then selected a second empty hive, assuring everybody that this one was free of both bees and wasps. It was brought out and opened up – and I can honestly say that the rat inside was as surprised as any of us! It ran for cover while the rest of us screamed. Everybody waited to see if the swarm would be tempted back into the newly prepared hives, instead of which, frustratingly for the watching crowd, it decided to move on and headed off in a great buzzing, swirling cloud, never to be seen again.

Since then, Sinyati, with regular help from David Njuguna, has gone from strength to strength. Honey production is steadily increasing, as are sales of the skin cream and the 'Sinyati A-Maizing' bee suits we taught them to make out of discarded maize sacks. And Bees Abroad recently paid for Walter Rono, the farm manager at the Cheptebo Rural Development Centre, to travel down to the National Beekeeping Station in Nairobi to give special training to two of Dave Bonner's Ugandan project leaders.

Most recently, the group has been short-listed for an award from the SEED Initiative, a global organisation that supports small scale innovative and sustainable development projects around the world aimed at alleviating poverty. Meanwhile, the members of the group are encouraging more women in the community to take up beekeeping by proving that it can work for them, with simple Kenyan top bar hives and home-made protective clothing at affordable prices enabling them to produce and sell their own honey and other hive products without any help from the men. One way and another, the Sinyati group seems to have all the makings of a prosperous little enterprise.

For Mary and me these out-of-the-way places in Kenya have become like a second home, our involvement with Bees Abroad giving us a new lease of life along with the added satisfaction of knowing that we are doing our bit, however small, to help some of the world's poorest, most underprivileged and yet most delightful and appreciative people.

Meanwhile, I still remain actively involved with the UK Bee Farmers Association. In fact, no sooner had I sold the business than I found myself back in office, becoming Chairman for the second time in 2009. More than twenty years after my first term of office ended, the particular problems and pressures faced by the beekeeping industry may have been a little different but the frustrations of failing to get the level of government support that we feel is so badly needed remained much the same.

The publicity generated in recent years by CCD and fears that the world's bee population is under some sort of serious environmental threat has certainly raised public awareness, to such an extent that Sarah Brown, wife of the former Prime Minister, hosted a special meeting at No 10 Downing Street while Labour was still in office at which representatives from a wide range of interested parties, including both the British Beekeepers Association and the UK Bee Farmers Association, the Bumblebee Society, Friends of the Earth and other environmental bodies got together with DEFRA officials and various government agricultural advisers and policy makers.

Me at No 10

On arrival, I and the other twenty or so people attending were first taken through the Cabinet Room and out into the No 10 gardens, where there were bumblebee nesting boxes but no hives. We were then led up the stairs, past the portraits of all previous Prime Ministers, to a room on the upper floor where a general debate took place. Everybody had their say about the environment and what could be done to make it more bee friendly, but nothing concrete resulted so that in the end one was left with the feeling that, sadly, it had been no more than a bit of window dressing.

During the rest of my two years as Chairman I was involved in further meetings with MPs at the House of Commons and also with Treasury officials in an effort, among other things, to secure assistance for beekeepers through such means as relief on fuel duty. On that particular issue, we made the point that although farmers don't have to pay duty on the 'red' diesel for their tractors, combine harvesters and other forms of farm machinery, bee farmers can't do beekeeping with a tractor. We need a different kind of dedicated vehicle and we argued that we should be able to get the same sort of tax relief on the fuel we used. But we didn't get anywhere with that.

The rather sad truth, I fear, is that because there are only about 300 full-time commercial bee farmers in this country we do not pack much of a punch when it comes to lobbying the powers that be. Even sadder is the fact that most people still don't seem fully to appreciate just how important bees are to the environment as a whole. It is estimated that one third of what we eat relies on pollination. You don't therefore have to be Einstein to work out that without bees we're all going to be in big trouble.

To end on a more positive note, I can truthfully say that I look back on my life as a beekeeper without the slightest regret, despite the often back-breaking work, the many challenges and the occasional frustrations, most of the latter caused by those civil servants who seem so determined to make things as difficult as possible for Britain's commercial bee farmers!

For me, beekeeping was a passion that became a profession and I count myself extremely fortunate to have been able to make a good living from what started out as a hobby. Especially since becoming involved with Bees Abroad, I have met so many different and interesting people over the years, ranging from show business personalities to royalty, and I have visited faraway places that I never dreamed I would ever set foot in. At the same time, Mary and I have gained immense satisfaction from being able to put our complementary skills to such good, worthwhile and hugely rewarding effect through our joint commitment to Bees Abroad.

Recipes

Candy bars and skin creams are among the hive products that Mary Home teaches Bees Abroad's African beekeepers to make, while Fosse Way's range of products included wood, furniture and floor polishes. For those readers who would like to try making any of these at home, here are the recipes.

Honey Peanut Candy

Ingredients

1 cup of dried milk powder
1 cup of honey
1 cup of peanut, almond or hazelnut butter (crunchy or smooth)
½ tsp vanilla/cocoa powder/coffee powder

For extra flavour try adding any of the following: sultanas, sesame seeds, sunflower seeds, chopped nuts or dried fruit.

Method

Mix all the ingredients together, shape into bite-sized pieces and refrigerate to make a great natural treat.

Beeswax furniture cream

Ingredients

2 lb 5 oz beeswax

8oz candle wax

5 pints pure gum turpentine

5 pints white spirits

2 ½ pints water

10 oz Lux soap flakes

½ pint white vinegar

Method

- Melt both waxes together to form liquid.
- Dissolve soap flakes in hot water.
- Warm turpentine and white spirit together until about 50°C.
- Add to melted wax.
- Then add soapy water, mixing vigorously.
- Finally add vinegar.

This makes a very large quantity of furniture cream but you can scale down the ingredients to meet your own requirements.

Precautions

Waxes and solvents are highly flammable and great care should be taken when heating them to avoid the risk of fire. Always use bain-marie water jacket containers to prevent direct heat being applied during the process.

Lotion Bars – Solid Skin Creams

Ingredients

1 part beeswax

1 part oil (maize oil/sunflower oil/olive oil/castor oil)

1 part solid butter (coconut butter/shea butter/avocado oil/cocoa butter/ mango butter or other luxury oils)

Fragrance oil of your choice (not essential)

Vitamin E oil (added as a preservative this is also excellent as a skin care product)

Essential oils of your choice (for example, neem oil for a bar to be used as an insect repellent) – one eighth of an ounce to 16 ounces of oils (in proportion 1:128)

Equipment and guidelines

- Moulds – soap moulds, jelly moulds, baking tray for small buns, anything with a suitable shape and size that is flexible.
- Plastic zip-lock bags or cellophane wrapping.
- A small decorative tin that can be re-used (adds to the value).
- Scales and measuring jug.
- Double boiler (bain-marie – little pan in a larger pan of water on a low heat – never melt waxes on a direct heat).

Make in small quantities unless adequate cool storage is available.

Method

- Weigh all your ingredients.
- Combine the oil and beeswax in the double boiler over a gentle heat until the wax is completely melted.
- Remove from the heat and add the remaining ingredients, stirring slowly until completely mixed.
- Pour carefully into moulds.
- Leave to cool for 3 hours. To save time it can be floated in cold water once the mixture has started to set.
- Pack as desired.

Advantages of a solid lotion bar

- Easy to create, using everyday equipment available in local stores (equipment should then only be used for cosmetic making and therefore kept separate from other kitchen utensils and free from dust).
- Ingredients also available in local food stores and chemists.
- Not complicated to make – easy to be creative.
- Product is convenient to use as the bar liquefies when rubbed between the hands and can be applied to rough or dry areas on the the lips, elbows or feet to keep skin hydrated.

Precautions

Waxes and solvents are highly flammable and great care should be taken when heating them to avoid the risk of fire. Always use bain-marie water jacket containers to prevent direct heat being applied during the process.

Home-made: Butcher's Arms
honey comes from its own hives

Here are three popular recipes from the Butcher's Arms restaurant at Priors Hardwick, near Southam in Warwickshire, which uses honey from its own hives.

Honey French Dressing

Ingredients
2 parts extra virgin olive oil
1 part vinegar
French mustard
honey
salt and pepper

Method
This is a recipe that is all done to personal taste. Firstly, put a tablespoon of honey, the olive oil and some French mustard into a blender, add salt and pepper and blend well, adding the vinegar a bit at a time. Adjust oil and vinegar according to taste.

The honey gives the dressing a distinctively sweet flavour to the dressing.

Honey and Whisky Ice Cream

Ingredients

300 ml double cream
60 ml whisky
60 ml liquid honey
4 large egg yolks

Method

- Whip the cream until it is thick, adding the whisky gradually.
- Put the honey into a small pan and heat it.
- Beat the egg yolks in a bowl.
- Pour the hot honey into the bowl containing the yolks and carry on beating the mixture until it is pale and thick.
- Gently fold in the cream and whisky mixture.
- Put the mixture in a freeze-proof container and freeze for at least three hours.

Guinness & Honey-glazed Pork Loin

To serve 6

Ingredients
300 ml Guinness
100 ml clear honey
250 g light Muscovado sugar
2 kg loin of pork
splash white wine
few sprigs of flat leaf parsley

Method
- To make the glaze, put the Guinness, honey and sugar into a pan.
  Reduce by almost half to form a sweet syrupy glaze then allow to cool.
- Heat oven to 200°C/fan gas 6. Season the pork with pepper and salt and
  roast on a baking tray for 20 minutes.
- Turn heat down to 160°C/fan gas 3. Remove the pork and brush all over
  with the glaze, reserving a few tablespoonfuls for later. Cook for a further
  40-50 minutes, brushing and basting the pork as it cooks until beautifully
  caramelised and glazed.
- Remove the pork from the roasting tray and leave to rest. Pour the
  remaining glaze into the roasting tray and then add the wine. Place
  the pan on the heat and bring everything to the boil. Simmer for a few
  minutes until you have thick gravy. Carve the pork into thick slices.
  Glaze with the Guinness syrup, drizzle a little onto the plates and finish
  with a sprig of parsley.